MILK FROM GRASS

(2ND EDITION)

Edited by

C. THOMAS, A. REEVE

and

G. E. J. FISHER

(Published 1991)

Published Jointly by:

ICI AGRICULTURAL DIVISION, PO BOX 1, BILLINGHAM, CLEVELAND TS23 1LB
and
THE SCOTTISH AGRICULTURAL COLLEGE, CLEEVE GARDENS, OAKBANK ROAD,
PERTH PH1 1HF
and
INSTITUTE OF GRASSLAND AND ENVIRONMENTAL RESEARCH, HURLEY,
MAIDENHEAD, BERKSHIRE SL6 5LR

Copies can be obtained from:

THE BRITISH GRASSLAND SOCIETY
NO 1 EARLEY GATE, UNIVERSITY OF READING RG6 2AT
Telephone: 0734 318189 Fax: 0734 666941

Bulk orders and student rates available.

ISBN 1 85482 261 6

Printed by Billingham Press Limited • 155 Central Avenue • Billingham • Cleveland • TS23 1LR

CONTENTS

ACKNOWLEDGEMENTS

We wish to thank the Agricutlural Research Institute of Northern Ireland for their major contribution to this edition. The hard work of ADAS and IGER staff in conducting the Grassland Manuring (GM) experiments, which provided data for the setting of fertilizer requirements is gratefully acknowledged. We wish to thank Miss D. H. Roberts of IGER for her excellent drawings of the stages of grass growth and Dr. D. Barraclough of Reading University for information on nitrate leaching. Thanks also to Miss Anne Dowdeswell for proof reading the final draft.

G.E.J. Fisher

A. Reeve

C. Thomas

FOREWORD

Since publication of the first edition of 'Milk From Grass' there have been substantial developments in the understanding of how management modifies grass growth and influences the farming environment. For example, much more is known about the response of plants to nitrogen and the extent to which nitrogen losses can occur. Consequently, representatives of ICI plc, The Scottish Agricultural College, the Agricultural Research Institute, Northern Ireland and Institute of Grassland and Environmental Research have combined to harness their research, advisory and practical experience in the efficient production and utilisation of grassland for milk production in a new edition of the booklet.

Four major considerations have influenced the new recommendations made on nitrogen usage. Firstly, a fuller statistical analysis of responses has highlighted the importance of the direct and interactive effects of nitrogen, summer rainfall and soil water. Thus, the classification of farms by site class has been maintained, but modified to reflect more accurately differences in yield potential. Secondly, the responses upon which recommendations are now based take account of the findings from the recent National Grassland Manuring Experiments, GM24, which established responses on swards grazed by cattle. Thirdly, the importance of previous cropping and grazing on the nitrogen status of the soil has been recognised and, finally, the need to use nitrogen responsibly in relation to the environment is emphasized.

In conforming to new codes of good practice, dairy farmers will have to pay closer attention to the control of silage effluent and the use of absorbents to reduce effluent production is discussed. The recent increase in the use of forage buffers for feeding grazing cows is addressed and recommendations for employing this management strategy are given. The resurgence of interest in mixed grass/white clover swards, as an alternative to fertilizer nitrogen, is covered by additions to every chapter. Additions have also been made to cover the management of summer calving cows, which are increasing in numbers in response to changes in the pricing structures of the Milk Marketing Boards.

This publication, as its predecessor, has chapters on grass production, winter feeding, grazing, the integration of grazing and cutting and economics. While every chapter has been updated to provide the latest thinking in these areas, the information is still presented in a succinct form. In doing so, each chapter highlights the general principles involved in the complex business of growing grass and using herbage efficiently.

At a time when production costs are rising faster than returns, attention to detail in management is becoming ever more important. It is hoped that this publication will indicate ways of achieving more efficient use of resources on dairy farms, and thus help to meet the challenge of the future.

CHAPTER 1

GRASS PRODUCTION
Dick Baker, Chris Doyle and Hector Lidgate

1.1 Patterns of Grass Growth and Yield
1.2 Environmental Effects
1.3 Sward type
1.4 Choice of D-value
1.5 Nitrogen for Grassland
1.6 Other Major Nutrients
1.7 Slurry
1.8 Conclusions

This chapter describes the potential of grass as a feed for dairy cows. It shows the basic pattern of grass growth and the factors which affect yield, and feeding value. Subsequent chapters deal with the management of grass, and how better use can be made of pastures for milk production.

1.1 PATTERNS OF GRASS GROWTH AND YIELD

A grass sward is made up of many individual tillers (shoots) and it is continually changing in response to the time of year and to the management which is imposed. In early spring growth is rapid, but as the days lengthen and temperatures rise the tillers begin to produce flower heads which would eventually seed if the crop was not cut or grazed (Figure 1.1).

Figure 1.1 Stages of Grass Growth, when the sward is allowed to develop without cutting or grazing (mid/late flowering perennial ryegrass). Early and leafy growth (D-value 70-75)

1

Lengthening of stems (D-value 67-70)

Flowering heads emerged (D-value 64-67)

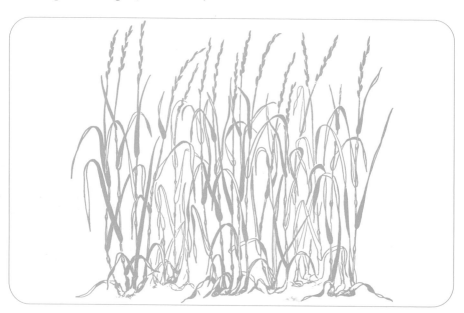

Mature crop (D-value 61-64)

The actual rate at which grass grows is a function of the environment, nutrient supply and the amount of leaf within the sward which is intercepting light. On any given day the rates of growth occurring in different fields will depend upon the date of the last harvest and whether harvesting is intermittent, as in conservation and rotational grazing, or more frequent, as for fields grazed continuously. Following defoliation there is typically a period of slow growth followed by an accelerating daily rate of growth, in some instances up to 200 kg dry matter per hectare (ha), and finally a period of decreasing growth as the grass canopy matures. The rate at which regrowth occurs is influenced markedly by the maturity of the crop at harvest. Following the harvesting of young leafy material the amount of leaf left behind is greater than when mature herbage is taken. The number of tiller growing points that are able to develop quickly is also greater. Consequently, the lag phase in growth is less following the harvesting of young material (Figure 1.2).

3

Figure 1.2   The influence of maturity on the rate of regrowth.

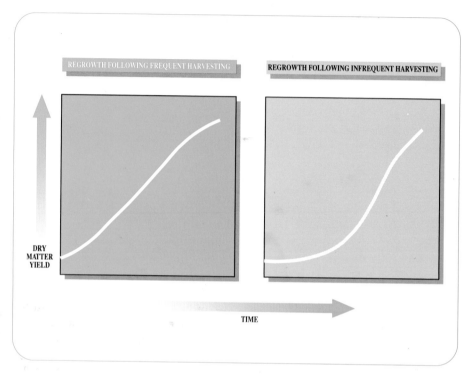

Grass grows more rapidly in spring when flower heads are developing but this growth potential can only be exploited at the expense of quality. Two important changes take place.

● Feed value falls as a grass tiller matures because it's fibre content rises and this fibre becomes lignified (woody).

● Non flowering tillers die as yield is allowed to build up in the field. The effect is a thinner sward which:

  ❑ is slower to regrow

  ❑ may allow weeds to establish

  ❑ is less resistant to poaching and may be less persistent; in extreme cases, reseeding is necessary to maintain production

Changes in maturity are also accompanied by changes in crude protein content. Typical values for perennial ryegrass are shown in Figure 1.3.

Figure 1.3 Changes in dry matter yield, D-value and crude protein content during uninterrupted primary growth

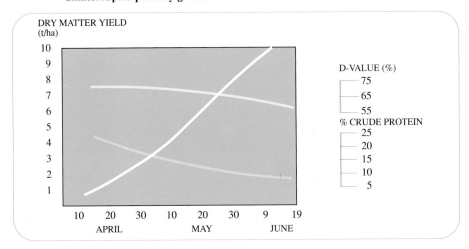

It can be seen that the feed value, in terms of both D-value and crude protein content, falls as grass is allowed to bulk-up for a conservation cut.

To manage grass effectively and to make sure of full utilisation a balance must be achieved between increasing herbage yield and falling quality. The way in which grass is managed and harvested also has a major influence on the seasonal pattern of production. Typical patterns develop for each management system and those for a 4-weekly overlapping sequence of cuts and for swards harvested under a continuous stocking management system are illustrated in Figure 1.4.

Figure 1.4 Seasonal pattern of herbage removal under cutting and under continuous grazing

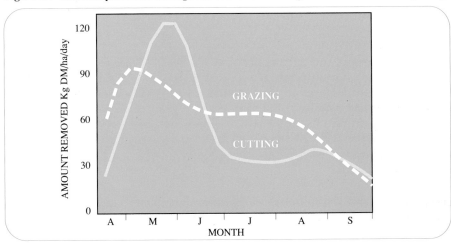

5

1.2 ENVIRONMENTAL EFFECTS

The 'Environment' includes the weather and the soil. The growth of all plants is affected by weather in the form of:

- **Radiation** - the amount of energy received from the sun
- **Temperature** - all plants need a certain minimum temperature to start growth in spring
- **Water** - supplied by rainfall and stored in the soil.

Grass grows well throughout lowland Britain and variations in radiation and temperature have only a relatively small effect on annual yield from one area to another. For example, variations in spring temperature influence the early yield but the effect on heading dates and subsequent yield of conservation crops is small, especially with late maturing varieties of grass.

The rate at which grass grows is determined by many factors. Whilst the level of available nutrients, water, sunlight and temperature are the most important, the frequency of harvesting has a considerable modifying effect by influencing the amount of leaf available to intercept light. For grazed swards the severity of defoliation also influences the amount of grass available. When grazing is too severe growth will be depressed, whereas grazing management which is too lax results in a wastage of herbage through death and decay (see page 59).

Reasonable estimates of the potential yields attainable on farms and the optimal level of nitrogen to apply on grassland can be made from a knowledge of summer rainfall, assessments of the soil nitrogen status and available water capacity of the soil, as indicated by soil texture.

(a) Rainfall

Rainfall during April to September varies from year to year and in different parts of the country (Figure 1.5).

(b) Soil type

Soils can be classified both in terms of texture and depth. Some soils can retain more water than others and crops grown on these soils are less susceptible to drying out. The ability to hold water is known as **'water holding capacity'** and when it is fully charged it is said to be at **'field capacity'**. The water holding capacity of a soil is determined by its texture (the proportions of sand, silt and clay which it contains) and by its depth. Deep soils will normally hold 120-165 mm of water whereas shallow soils over rock or gravelly and coarse soils will hold 40-80 mm.

(c) Soil N Status

Yields on farms are greatly influenced by the level of nitrogen used and the nitrogen status of the soil. This is measured as the amount of nitrogen harvested if no fertilizer N is applied.

Figure 1.5 Average rainfall (mm) from April to September

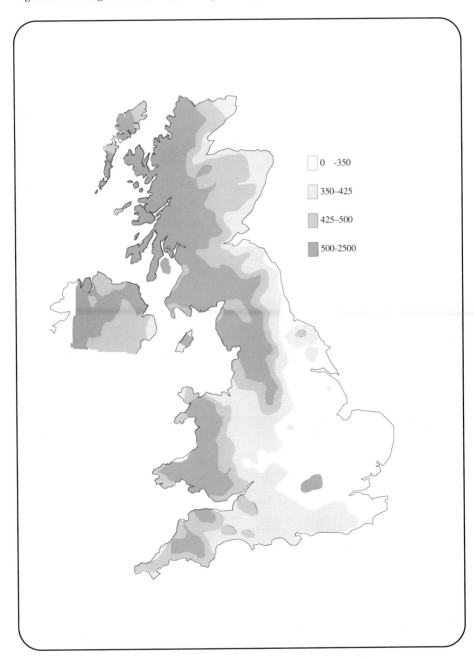

0   -350

350–425

425–500

500-2500

Recent field studies by ADAS have shown that soil nitrogen status is mainly influenced by previous management. Typical values range from 30-80 kg N/ha following 1-2 year leys in an arable rotation and for poor permanent pasture, to 80-160 kg N/ha for well fertilized leys and permanent pasture, and up to 200 kg N/ha if permanent pasture is ploughed out and re-sown. For simplicity, soil nitrogen status is adjudged to be low, medium, or high (Table 1.1). Soil N status has a marked affect on the responses to fertilizer nitrogen and as it increases the response decreases so that less fertilizer is required to obtain the same total yield.

Table 1.1. Soil nitrogen status

Soil N Status	Previous Management
Low	● Cereal cropping or short term ley having received less than 250 Kg N/ha. ● Poor quality permanent grassland receiving less than 100 Kg N/ha.
Medium	● Permanent grassland or long term ley having received 100-250 Kg N/ha. ● Grass/arable land receiving more than 250 kg N/ha.
High	● Permanent grassland or long term ley receiving more than 250 kg N/ha. ● Permanent grassland receiving large amounts of slurry. ● Permanent grassland containing large amounts of clover.

(d) Determination of Grass Growing Conditions

Summer rainfall and soil texture are the best indicators of grass growing conditions. They can be used to classify farms or parts of farms on the basis of 'site classes' on a scale of 1 (very good) to 5 (poor), as indicated in Table 1.2.

Most soils are at field capacity in the spring and this means that, even in the driest areas, there will be almost a full yield of grass for grazing or cutting until late May. The major differences in grass growing conditions due to water shortage normally occur in the June to August period. The effect is to limit the response to nitrogen and thus it is greatest at high levels of nitrogen use.

Table 1.2. Site classes

Soil Texture	Average April-September Rainfall			
	More than 500 mm	425-500 mm	350-425 mm	Less than 350 mm
All soils except shallow soils over chalk/rock or gravelly and coarse sandy soils	1	2	2	3
Shallow soils over chalk or rock and gravelly and coarse sandy soils	2	3	4	5

8

(e) Potential Yield

The annual grass yields for each site class which may be achieved or exceeded in 8 years out of 10 are shown in Table 1.3. These values are for fields cut for silage (conserved) or grazed (cut at monthly intervals - simulated grazing).

The yields indicated do not represent amounts that may be consumed. Under both grazing and cutting, losses will occur due either to senescence and decay on grazed pastures or to physical, respiration and fermentation losses in conservation. Efficiency of utilisation under both grazing and conservation is affected greatly by the managements adopted.

Table 1.3 Probable yields of grass when cut for conservation or to simulate grazing (based on medium N status and optimal N per cut)

Site class	Dry matter yield (t/ha)		
	Conserved (2 cuts at 61D)*	Conserved (3 cuts at 68D)**	Grazed
1	16.0	15.4	14.3
2	15.4	14.4	12.8
3	14.3	13.4	11.4
4	13.4	12.6	10.5
5	12.6	11.7	9.6

* Cuts taken on 10 June, 12 August, followed by grazing
** Cuts taken on 18 May, 22 June, 27 July, followed by autumn grazing

The first part of this chapter has shown that the availability of water affects grass growth. However, this factor is mainly outside the control of most farmers. Other factors which have a direct effect on grass growth and which can be controlled are:

● the types of grasses which are grown

● the levels of fertilizer which are used

● the general management (e.g. how often the grass is cut or grazed, when the fertilizer is applied).

Factors such as these have a major effect on the yield, the distribution of this yield throughout the growing season and the persistency of the sward.

1.3 SWARD TYPE

There are a wide range of grasslands in the British Isles but they can be broadly divided into short and long term leys and permanent grassland.

(a) Leys

These have high yields, are relatively easy to manage and have a good feed value for livestock. The most important species used are perennial and Italian ryegrasses. Other species such as timothy, meadow fescue, tall fescue and cocksfoot are used less today but are still appropriate in certain circumstances.

(i) *Species*

There is little to choose between the sown grass species in terms of total annual yield but there are differences in features such as:

- ❏   rate of establishment
- ❏   seasonality of growth
- ❏   drought tolerance
- ❏   ease of management
- ❏   persistency
- ❏   palatability
- ❏   feed value

Italian ryegrass develops most rapidly after sowing. It grows early in spring and gives higher yields in the first year than perennial ryegrass but it is relatively short-lived. Perennial ryegrass also develops rapidly from seed, compared to other perennial species, and its annual yield is generally high. In terms of the seasonal distribution of growth the cultivated species differ in the timing of spring growth and the date of peak rate of production. However, such differences are small and much less than might be expected from their heading dates.

Perennial ryegrass is more digestible at a given stage of maturity than other sown perennial grasses. This, combined with a good yield, means that the highest yields at a given digestibility come from this grass.

(ii) *Varieties*

The choice of variety has often been the subject of complicated advice. In fact it should be a simple matter. The main distinction between sown varieties is the time of heading and it is this which can be exploited to spread the harvesting period. Detailed descriptions of the recommended varieties and their heading categories can be found in the NIAB Farmers Leaflet, Number 2. This publication can be obtained from the National Institute of Agricultural Botany, Huntingdon Road, Cambridge. In Scotland, information on recommended varieties can be obtained from the 'Classification of Grass and Clover Varieties for Scotland' publication, via Scottish Agricultural College offices. In Northern Ireland, DANI guidelines on recommended grass varieties are published annually in the May issue of 'Agriculture in Northern Ireland.'

Seed mixtures should be kept fairly simple so that they have a predictable performance and are easily managed. The temptation to mix very early and very late grasses should be avoided. If a spread of harvesting dates is desired this can be achieved by using different varieties, with different heading dates, in **different** fields.

Under lowland conditions, yield, quality, persistency and flexibility for most purposes will be found in later heading varieties of perennial ryegrass. Early varieties of perennial ryegrass, hybrid or Italian ryegrasses need only be considered when early production or a short term ley is required.

In this booklet it is assumed that the grassland for which the potential is described is perennial ryegrass or at least mainly perennial ryegrass.

(b) Permanent Grassland

(i) *Content of Grass Sward*
Over half of lowland grass used by dairy cows is unsown or sown more than 10 years ago. These swards contain a wide range of species and some are capable, in favourable conditions, of yields similar to those of perennial ryegrass. However under intensive use it is perennial ryegrass which persists and remains productive and the value of old pastures in lowland conditions is related to the content of perennial ryegrass.

(ii) *Improving Grass Swards*
When grassland contains the less productive species reseeding is not always possible, neither is it the only way to improve production. A simple change in management can often result in dramatic improvements in sward quality. Frequent and close grazing will encourage the more productive species if deficiencies in lime, phosphate and potash have been corrected and if sufficient nitrogen is applied. Many permanent pastures already contain some perennial ryegrass and this will be encouraged by good management. Improvement of pastures by this means can have many advantages. For example, there will be:

❏   no loss of production during reseeding

❏   none of the cost directly associated with reseeding

❏   less risk of poaching which is sometimes associated with grazing a new ley

(c) White Clover

There is increasing interest in the use of mixed grass/white clover swards as an alternative or complement to grass pastures which receive high rates of fertilizer nitrogen (grass/nitrogen). This comes from an awareness of possible pollution problems from nitrates when high rates of nitrogen are applied to agricultural land and the possibility that future legislation may restrict the amount of nitrogen fertilizers which can be used.

The agronomy of grass/clover swards is very different from grass/nitrogen pastures and they require different considerations in management. For example, white clover needs higher temperatures for growth than grass and the seasonal increase in growth rate of clover therefore occurs later than the surge of grass growth in spring. This 'delay' in the annual growth of clover makes it tempting to apply nitrogen to mixed swards in the spring to gain a significant 'early bite' of grass. However, clover will make use of this nitrogen and clover nitrogen fixation will be reduced. Consequently, the amount of clover in the pasture will diminish, as will its contribution to total yield and input of nitrogen to the grass. This dilemma is illustrated in Figure 1.6 and the effect of nitrogen on sward clover content is shown in Table 1.4.

Figure 1.6   Average daily growth rate of grass and white clover in grass/clover swards at two annual fertilizer N rates

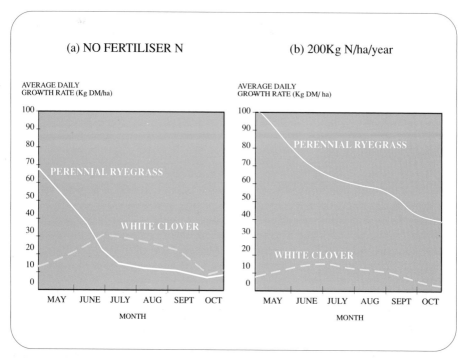

When clover provides a good ground cover of stolon and can reach a peak content in a mixed sward of over 20 % of the total dry matter, it is capable of fixing 150-200 Kg nitrogen/ha. It is only at very low levels of fertilizer input, or where no fertilizer nitrogen is used, that clover makes a substantial contribution to total yield. At the target levels of fertilizer nitrogen recommended in this book of 270 to 390 Kg/ha (average grass growing conditions) white clover will not make a significant contribution to the yield of the sward. This can be seen in Figure 1.7, which demonstrates that above 200-300 Kg nitrogen/ha, total yield is not improved by including clover in the sward.

Table 1.4. Effect of fertilizer nitrogen application rates on white clover performance in grass/clover swards.

Fertilizer N (Kg/ha/year)	DM (t/ha/year)		
	Total herbage	White clover	White clover (%)
0	7.83	4.14	53
120	8.71	2.43	28
240	9.98	1.07	11
360	11.70	0.51	4
	(Frame, SAC)		

Figure 1.7 Average total herbage production from perennial ryegrass (cv. Aberystwyth S23 and grass (cv. S23)/white clover (cv. Aberstwyth S100) swards

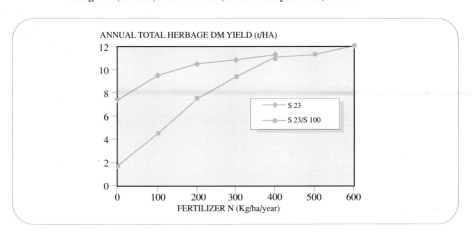

White clover, however, is encouraged by close grazing with cattle and when management favours the growth and persistence of clover, this legume may contribute to the feed value of the herbage by supplying extra protein, energy and minerals.

With no fertilizer nitrogen input the yield of a grass clover sward is likely to be 70-80% of that achieved at the target nitrogen usage for each site class. This is demonstrated in Table 1.5. The average yield from three cuts of a grass/white clover sward with no fertilizer nitrogen was 71% (8.3 t DM/ha) of the yield from a grass sward receiving 340 Kg nitrogen/ha (11.7 t DM/ha).

There is little information on the herbage production of grass/clover swards under dairy cattle grazing. However, experience from many areas of the UK suggests that a well managed mixed pasture will carry 65-75% of the stocking rate of a grass/nitrogen sward over a grazing season.

While reliance on grass/clover swards not receiving fertilizer nitrogen can prove financially acceptable (see Chapter 5, page 101) such systems carry a risk of not having herbage available as required due to the variability of clover content between seasons and the delayed growth habit of this legume. However, new and more persistent cultivars of clover are now available and it is clear that close attention must be given to soil fertility if clover is to persist and the need for frequent reseeding avoided (see Section 1.6).

Table 1.5   Annual yields of herbage from a three-cut system of grass/nitrogen (340 Kg N/ha/year) and grass/white clover (0 Kg N/ha/year).

Year	Herbage yield (t DM/ha)	
	Grass/nitrogen	Grass/white clover
1985	12.63	9.36
1986	10.87	7.04
1987	11.63	8.45
Mean 1985-87	11.71	8.29

(Roberts, SAC)

1.4 CHOICE OF D VALUE

The timing of harvests must be a compromise between quality and quantity. To obtain a higher digestibility (D value) grass must be harvested more frequently. The example in Figure 1.8 shows how cutting at various digestibilities affects yield at each cut and over the year. If grass is cut at high quality some loss of yield must be accepted. This applies to all site classes and the size of the crops to be expected at each site class under different conservation managements is shown in Appendix 1.1

It should be noted, however, that the size and maturity of a conservation crop affects the rate of recovery. This can be important in meeting requirements for summer grazing. When a cut is taken at high quality the delay in growth is minimal, but removing a heavy crop at low D value can cause a severe setback and may make the sward more open for some months afterwards. The removal of a crop at about 68 D results in a delay of approximately 1 week in regrowth compared to a normal grazing cycle while cutting a crop at 61D will delay regrowth by two weeks. The effect of cutting frequency on the subsequent use of grass for grazing is discussed in Chapter 4.

Figure 1.8 The effect of cutting at various digestibilities on the yield of grass at site class 3.

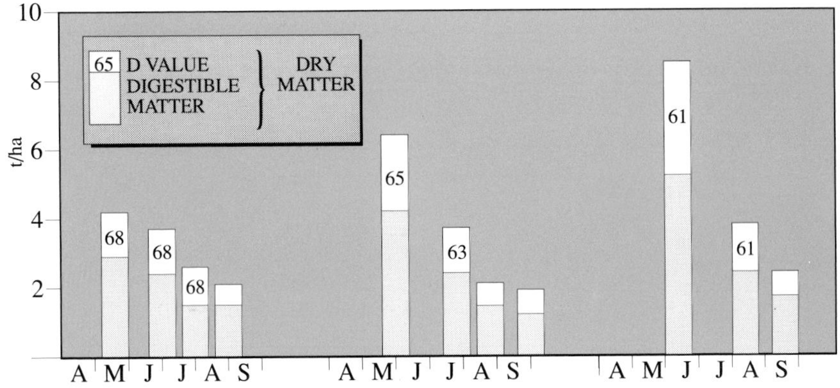

	3 CUTS HIGH QUALITY	2 CUTS MEDIUM QUALITY	2 CUTS LOW QUALITY
DRY MATTER YIELD t / ha / yr	13.3	13.9	14.5
DIGESTIBLE MATTER YIELD t / ha / yr	9.3	9.6	9.1

1.5 NITROGEN FOR GRASSLAND

Grass requires a good supply of all three major nutrients; nitrogen (N), phosphorus (P) and potassium (K). Of these three, nitrogen is the most important in determining yield but the response to nitrogen depends on an adequate supply of other nutrients and on the site class of the field.

Average rates of nitrogen fertilizer currently applied to grassland on dairy farms are about 200 kg N/ha and there is scope to increase the yield of grass by applying more. However, higher levels must be used responsibly to avoid unacceptable losses of nitrogen and adverse environmental effects.

(a) Rate of Application

Grass responds to fertilizer nitrogen in a characteristic way. The response is almost linear up to applications of 200-300 kg N/ha/year depending on the site and management adopted. The yield increase in this phase will be about 15-30 kg dry matter per ha per kg of additional nitrogen depending on soil nitrogen status. Thereafter the response begins to decline until a maximum yield is reached at about 500-850 kg N/ha.

The point where the response drops to 7.5 kg dry matter of grass per ha for each kg of nitrogen which is applied is defined as the target yield and target nitrogen rate for dairying.

15

At this level 90% of maximum yield will be achieved with less than 60% of the nitrogen needed to achieve maximum yield. Whilst small economic gains may occur from applications beyond the target levels, much of the nitrogen will be used inefficiently and result in increasing and unacceptable losses to the atmosphere and to ground water.

The general form of response is shown in Figure 1.9 and the difference in the response between site classes in Figure 1.10.

Figure 1.9   General form of response of grass to fertilizer nitrogen.

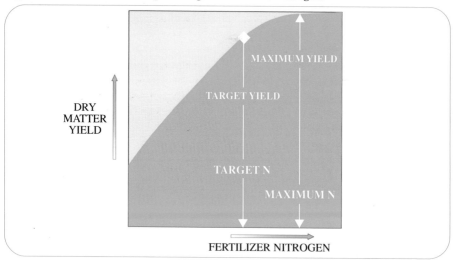

Figure 1.10 Yield and response of grass cut six times at 4 weekly intervals (simulated grazing) to fertilizer nitrogen according to site class assuming a medium soil N status.

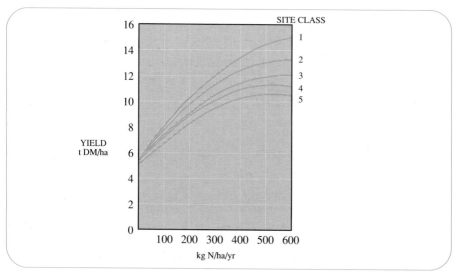

The appropriate target levels for nitrogen use depend, in general, on:

- site class (growing conditions)
- soil nitrogen status
- sward management (grazing or cutting)

However, some farmers will need to take account of current and prospective legislation for nitrate sensitive areas (NSA) and voluntary codes of practice for environmentally sensitive areas (ESA). Where restrictions are in force the recommendation is to apply most of the permitted amount early in the season.

Examples of the effects of these three factors on the recommended rates of nitrogen application are shown in Tables 1.6-1.8. Detail of the pattern of nitrogen applications which should ensure that the marginal response does not fall below 7.5 Kg dry matter per Kg nitrogen for grazing, 2 cut conservation and 3 cut conservation systems, are given in Appendix 1.2.

(i) *The Effect of Site Class*

The more favourable the site class (grass growing conditions - see Table 1.2) the more the applied fertilizer nitrogen will be utilised. This influence on nitrogen application rates is shown in Table 1.6.

Table 1.6   The effect of site class on total nitrogen applications for grazing (assuming medium soil N status).

Site class	Total N application (Kg N/ha)
1	430
2	380
3	320
4	300
5	255

(ii) *The Effect of Soil Nitrogen Status*

The higher the soil nitrogen supply (see Table 1.1), the less fertilizer nitrogen is needed to achieve target yield. This is demonstrated in Table 1.7.

(iii) *The Effect of Sward Management*

Whether a sward is grazed or cut will influence the amount of fertilizer nitrogen required to obtain target yield. In most dairy farming systems in the UK the major management factors are grazing, 2 conservation cuts and 3 conservation cuts, as shown in Table 1.8.

Table 1.7   The effect of soil nitrogen status on total nitrogen applications for grazing (assuming site class 3).

Soil N status	Total N application (Kg N/ha)
HIGH	270
MEDIUM	320
LOW	390

Table 1.8   The effect of sward management on total nitrogen applications (assuming site class 3 and medium soil N supply).

Management	Total N application (Kg N/ha)
Grazing	320
2 conservation cuts	330
3 conservation cuts	380

(b) Nitrogen Use and the Environment

All soils contain substantial amounts of nitrogen ranging from 4-20 tonnes per hectare down to a depth of 30 cm. However, 99% is in an organic form and is not directly available to plants. Chemical and microbial activity within the soil releases nitrogen as ammonium (mineralization) which may be converted to nitrate (nitrification). Both ammonium and nitrate ions, from mineralization or from excreta or fertilizer, are available for plant uptake, but nitrate may be lost by leaching into drainage or ground waters, or by conversion into nitrous oxide and nitrogen gases (denitrification). The relative proportions lost through denitrification and leaching will vary considerably according to soil type with higher leaching losses on free draining soils and higher denitrification losses on poorly drained soils.

The use of fertilizer nitrogen markedly increases the levels of ammonium and nitrate in the soil but as levels rise the proportion used by plants falls. Initially, losses increase slowly as more fertilizer nitrogen is applied, but ultimately a breakpoint is reached and thereafter they rise rapidly, particularly losses due to leaching (Figure 1.11). Losses are likely to become unacceptable on environmental grounds once annual applications exceed 250-390 kg N/ha depending on the management practice adopted. The break points are lower on grazed than cut swards as nitrogen returned in dung and urine may vary from 100 to over 300 kg at low and high N usage. Much of the nitrogen in urine is in the form of urea which may be lost as ammonia through volatilization although this loss is often low and equivalent to less than 5% of the fertilizer applied. Typical values for nitrogen fluxes in a grazed sward at site class 3 are shown in Figure 1.12.

18

Figure 1.11 Nitrate leaching under grazed (■) and cut (▲) grass over three years

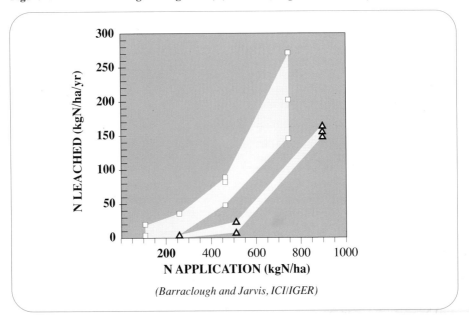

(Barraclough and Jarvis, ICI/IGER)

Figure 1.12 The Nitrogen Cycle. Typical values for a long term ley on a loamy soil with moderate drainage in Site Class 3 when grazed by cattle and receiving target N (Kg N/ha)

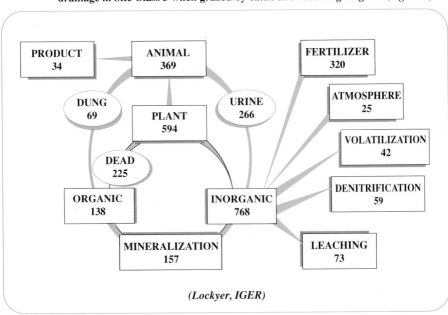

(Lockyer, IGER)

19

There are three factors besides the total rate of application, which can be considered by any dairy farmer and which might contribute to reducing environmental pollution from nitrogen usage:

- timing of initial spring applications
- timing of final applications in late season
- type of fertilizer nitrogen used

(i) *Timing of Initial Applications*

The date when nitrogen fertilizer is first applied in a season is important as the interaction between this timing and temperature can be crucial in obtaining maximum dry matter production and avoiding losses of nitrogen through denitrification and leaching. The method used to predict the optimum time for first application has been the 'T sum 200,' which is supposed to indicate when grass starts to grow. It is defined as the date when the sum of the average daily temperatures above $0°C$, since January 1st, reaches $200°C$. If nitrogen fertilizer is applied before the start of grass growth, unacceptable losses to the environment may occur.

Much work has gone into assessing the use of T sum in the UK. The main conclusion is that the method is of limited use in an island temperate climate, such as experienced in the UK. This is because there is wide variation from year to year in the pattern of temperature rise from 1st January. Consequently, in some years T sum 200 is reached long before ground conditions permit the application of fertilizer, while in others it arrives long after the first dressing should sensibly be applied.

T sum 200 can not be taken as a specific guide of when to apply the first dressing of nitrogen. There is, however, normally a 2-5 week period in which applications will produce yields above 90% of the maximum. On most farms T sum 200 will fall within this period and it can therefore be used as an indicator of when to apply a first dressing. To avoid losses to the environment and make maximum use of fertilizer, the first dressing of nitrogen can be made from mid February onwards (early March onwards for most of northern England and Scotland) when ground conditions permit and when T sum has reached $180-200°C$. It should be noted, however, that T sum can vary markedly in individual areas of the country, depending on local topography.

(ii) *Timing of Final Applications*

Grass will utilise applied fertilizer nitrogen as long as conditions are favourable for grass growth. Loss of nitrogen to the environment will occur in late season, if more nitrogen than can be utilised is applied when grass growth is declining rapidly. To avoid this pollution risk, it is recommended that no fertilizer nitrogen is applied after mid August and applications in early August should be kept to a maximum of 50 Kg N/ha for silage aftermaths, and 40 Kg N/ha for previously grazed swards. More details can be found in Appendix 1.2.

(iii) *Type of Nitrogen Fertilizer*

The most common nitrogen fertilizers in use are based on ammonium nitrate, calcium ammonium nitrate, urea and anhydrous ammonia. Those which contain, or generate, only ammonium nitrogen cause the lowest losses through denitrification and leaching. Losses of 10-30% from spring applications by denitrification of nitrate have been detected with fertilizers not based on ammonium nitrogen, which results in:

- pollution of the environment
- less nitrogen available for grass growth

Recently, urea has come into common use for spring applications, because it can show a small advantage in yield at this time compared to other forms of nitrogen. Significant amounts of nitrogen may however be lost through volatilization of ammonia. Losses through denitrification are negligible with urea, but this gain is offset by the loss of ammonia. In most studies in Europe, calcium ammonium nitrate is superior to urea in both yield of grass produced and minimising losses to the environment.

1.6 OTHER MAJOR NUTRIENTS

The first part of this chapter has dealt with the affects of climate and nitrogen supply on the growth of grass. It cannot be over-emphasized that the growth rates and nitrogen responses shown are only achieved when other aspects of soil fertility are not limiting. It is important, therefore. that soil pH, phosphorus and potassium status be maintained at satisfactory levels and checked routinely at three to five year intervals by soil analysis.

(a) Lime

The grasses sown in modern swards grow best, and with a nutritionally satisfactory mineral content, when the soil pH is maintained near to 6.0. Soils in the UK tend to become acid naturally due to the acidifying effect of rainfall.

Fertilizers can also affect the soil pH. Nitrogen fertilizers based on ammonium salts reduce soil pH (increase acidity). Some products (ammonium sulphate and ammonium phosphate) have a greater effect on soil pH than others (ammonium nitrate, urea) whilst nitrate based products (e.g. sodium nitrate) increase soil pH. Ammonium nitrate applied as 34% nitrogen product reduces soil pH, whilst calcium ammonium nitrate products are less acidifying.

When soil testing shows pH to be 5.7 or below, lime should be applied to restore the soil pH to the 6.0-6.5 range. Over-liming should be avoided as this will reduce the availability of the important trace elements copper and manganese to the herbage and to the detriment of animal performance. It is also crucial to maintain soil pH above 6.0 if clover is to persist in mixed swards.

(b) Phosphorus

Phosphorus applications should be based on maintaining a soil phosphorus index of 2. Typically, grass herbage at the early silage cutting stage contains 0.6-0.8% P_2O_5 on a dry matter basis, resulting in an offtake of 30-40 kg/ha in a 5 tonnes dry matter/ha silage cut. A full season with 3 or 4 silage cuts can remove 80-100 kg/ha of P_2O_5. On most farms a proportion of this removal is returned via slurry and grazing. Annual applications of 40-70 kg/ha P_2O_5 are therefore usually adequate to maintain soil phosphorus on cutting ground. On grazing fields, because of the continual return of phosphorus in droppings, applications of 25-50 kg/ha P_2O_5 suffice. General recommendations for phosphorus applications to grassland based on soil analysis are presented in Tables 1.9 and 1.10.

Table 1.9 Phosphorous and potassium recommendations for grazed swards

	Soil P or K Indices			
	0	**1**	**2**	**over 2**
		P2O5 or K2O kg/ha		
Phosphorus	60	40	20	Nil
Potassium *	60	30	Nil	Nil

* To reduce the risk of hypomagnesaemia (grass staggers) potassium applications should not be made in spring except where soil potassium index is 0.

As a general rule the timing of phosphorus application has not been considered to be important. However, the phosphorus demand of the grass crop is greatest at times of maximum grass growth rates in spring. Experimental evidence shows that spring applications of phosphorus increase the phosphorus content of the herbage for silage making by about 10% as compared with no application. Since first cut silage is the major part of the silage production on most farms, this opportunity to increase silage phosphorus content may be nutritionally important as livestock production systems become more silage based. Similarly, in work with grazing livestock, the Scottish Agricultural College has shown that early spring phosphorus applications can increase grass production slightly and also the phosphorus content of the grass at the grazing stage. Thus, there may be an advantage in applying maintenance levels in spring rather than later on in the season.

Table 1.10 Phosphorous and potassium recommendations for cut swards

	Soil P or K Indices				
	0	**1**	**2**	**3**	**over 3**
One Cut – Hay or Silage		P_2O_5 or K_2O kg/ha			
Phosphorus	100	60	40	30	Nil
Potassium	100	75	60	30	Nil
Multi Cut Silage					
Phosphorus *					
Cut 1	100	60	40	20	Nil
per further cut	50	30	20	20	Nil
Potassium **					
Cut 1	100	75	60	30	Nil
per further cut	80	60	45	30	Nil

* It may be advantageous to apply the full amount of phosphorus for the year before the first cut.
** The most efficient use of potassium is achieved by applications for each cut.

(c) Potassium

The amount of potassium required by grass depends largely on whether it is to be grazed or cut.

(i) *Grazing*

Most of the potassium ingested by grazing livestock is excreted in their urine and so is returned to the grazed land. However, the return is not uniform, indeed it is very patchy and a proportion is exported in milk from dairy farms. With clay soils applications of 25-35 kg K_2O/ha should maintain the soil status. On sandy soils greater amounts may be needed to maintain the soil potassium index. Soil potassium index can build up rapidly to high levels under grazing and therefore regular soil testing is recommended. Potassium fertilizer recommendations for grazed swards are presented in Table 1.9.

In order to reduce the risk of hypomagnesaemia (grass staggers) potassium is not normally applied before spring grazing but preferably in mid-season.

High soil potassium indices of 3 or over are undesirable on grass/nitrogen swards because there is an increased risk of hypomagnesaemia with grazing livestock. In such circumstances potassium application should be omitted. However, attention should also be paid to the magnesium status of the soil and where hypomagnesaemia is known to occur applications of magnesium should be considered as well as the timing and rate of potassium to be applied.

(ii) *Cutting*

A great deal of potassium is removed in conservation cuts. For example, a silage crop of 5 tonnes dry matter/ha contains about 120 kg K_2O. The amount of potassium supplied by the soil is greatest for clay soils and least for sandy soils. On clay soils it is usually only necessary to provide about two-thirds of the crop potassium requirement. The soil will provide the remainder from soil reserves. Sandy soils have very little reserve of potassium and the crop requirement must be fully met from fertilizer and manure. Slurry is a useful source of potassium for grass which is to be conserved.

In cutting regimes potassium fertilizer is utilised most efficiently by applications at the start of each growth period. In general it should be applied at the rate of 0.5 kg K_2O for each Kg of nitrogen applied. Potassium fertilizer recommendations for cut swards are presented in Table 1.10.

(d) Grass/Clover Swards

While the above recommendations for phosphate and potash applications on grass swards aim to keep indices at level 2 (Tables 1.9 and 1.10), on grass/clover pastures the aim should be to maintain the soil index above 2.

Therefore, to manage a mixed sward to the benefit of clover, no nitrogen fertilizer should be applied and annual applications of up to 100 Kg P_2O_5/ha and 170 Kg K_2O/ha may be necessary. The returns of phosphorous and potassium through urine and faeces on grazed swards will reduce the levels required. However, emphasis must be placed on regular assessment of soil mineral status and maintenance of phosphate and potash indices if clover is to persist and provide for financially viable levels of herbage production.

(e) Sulphur

For many years there was sufficient sulphur deposited from the atmosphere to supply the sulphur needs of crops in the UK. However, since the introduction of regulations to minimise atmospheric pollution by smoke in the 1960's, sulphur deposition has declined so that in some areas sulphur deficiency has been observed in crops. The areas most susceptible to sulphur deficiency are mainly in the south and west of England and also the east of Scotland. Deficiency is most likely to occur on sandy or chalk soils, particularly where swards are mainly cut or in ley arable rotations. In these situations reductions in the yield of second and third cut crops of silage may occur if sulphur containing fertilizer is not applied. Regular applications of manures or slurry will also lessen the likelihood of sulphur deficiency. It has been demonstrated in Ireland that where sulphur is deficient the nutritional quality of silage, and of pasture is improved by sulphur applications.

In most situations application of 10 kg sulphur/ha at the start of the re-growth period will prevent any loss of grass production due to sulphur deficiency. It is preferable that the sulphur be applied in the sulphate form rather than as micronised sulphur sprayed onto the grass foliage. Direct uptake through the leaves is slight, and most uptake takes place through the plant roots in the sulphate form.

1.7 SLURRY

Slurry contains significant amounts of plant nutrients, especially potassium and nitrogen. With increasing concern about the pollution of water courses by slurry more emphasis is being given to better slurry storage facilities on farms. There should also be more emphasis on the use of slurry as a source of nutrient rather than as a nuisance to be disposed of. The handling, storage and use of slurry must conform with the Code of Good Agricultural Practice. Care must always be taken to avoid direct run-off of slurry to water courses, especially when ground is waterlogged or frozen, and slurry should never be spread within 10 m of any watercourse. Application rates should not exceed 250 Kg/ha/year of total nitrogen applied in manures, slurry and dirty water.

The chemical composition of slurry varies widely depending on storage conditions and the extent to which it is diluted with water. It is simpler to estimate the nutrients available in slurry on the farm from the likely output by the animals than by using published data on slurry composition (Table 1.11).

24

Table 1.11 The estimated output of nutrients in dung and urine by a cow over six months winter feeding.

Nutrient	Voided	In slurry Kg/cow
N	40	30
P_2O_5	15	15
K_2O	40	40
CaO	20	20
MgO	10	10

Some of the nitrogen, however, is lost through volatilisation of ammonia and some by denitrification in storage so that, even in a well designed slurry handling system, there is likely to be a 10-15% loss of the nitrogen content of cattle slurry to the atmosphere. The other nutrients can only be lost by leakage from slurry stores. Ammonia volatilisation can be reduced by covering the store, but this is unlikely to be economic. Following spreading on land, further losses will occur by volatilisation, denitrification and leaching of nitrates. Adding acid to slurry at this stage offers potential for reducing volatilisation losses, or alternatively slurry can be injected directly into the soil. Nitrification inhibitors will also delay the conversion of ammonium nitrogen to nitrate in the soil and have a role to play in reducing losses through denitrification and nitrate leaching. These techniques are still being researched.

Slurry should only be applied in amounts such that the nitrogen content can be utilised by the growing crop. The most efficient and environmentally least risky use of slurry is by ploughing into the land being prepared for late spring sown crops, such as maize, fodder beet or other spring planted arable crops.

To use slurry most effectively as a nutrient supply for grassland it is best applied to the conservation area in early spring as soon as ground conditions allow. If application is later than 8 weeks before harvesting it may adversely affect silage fermentation, or on grazing land it may lead to problems of grass rejection. If applications are made to grassland in autumn or winter, then most of the nitrogen content of slurry will be lost due to ammonia volatilisation, denitrification and leaching. Similarly, if very heavy applications of slurry are made to grassland in autumn prior to ploughing up and reseeding the sward, most of the nitrogen will be lost by leaching. An application of cow slurry to silage land in January to February is likely to reduce the fertilizer requirement by 30-40 Kg N/ha, 10-15 Kg P_2O_5/ha and 40-60 Kg K_2O/ha.

1.8 CONCLUSIONS

● The yield of grass varies according to the growing conditions (site class), the quality of the sward and the level of fertilizer nitrogen which is used.

- The site class of a grass field can be assessed from a knowledge of the summer rainfall and the soil type; the site class determines not only the potential total yield of grass but also the seasonal distribution of yield. There is little variation in spring growth between sites and the main differences between site classes occur in mid and late season.

- For most practical purposes the quality of a sward is assessed by its ryegrass content. Ryegrass will give the yield, quality, persistence and flexibility which is needed for high yielding swards.

- Target nitrogen fertilizer rates can be assessed for all site classes and management systems. There are great opportunities to increase the yields of grass on most dairy farms. However, increases in fertilizer usage should not be made without consideration of possible adverse environmental effects.

- As grass matures its feed value declines and there is a need to balance this against the fact that frequent harvesting reduces the total annual yield from a grass field. This is an important concept since the objective in growing grass is to feed cattle effectively, not simply to maximise yield.

- Mixed swards of grass/white clover may provide a viable alternative to grass/nitrogen pastures. If it is to persist, management must favour the clover, but a reduction in total herbage yield compared to grass/nitrogen pastures, with recommended rates of nitrogen applied, must be accepted.

Subsequent chapters deal with the feeding of grazed and conserved grass to dairy cows and with the effects of different forms of grassland management on yield and profit.

CHAPTER 2

FORAGE CONSERVATION AND WINTER FEEDING

Cledwyn Thomas and George Fisher

Efficient conservation is a vital part of grassland management. The objectives of forage conservation are to:-

● Produce a feed for the dairy cow during the winter with the minimum loss of quality and quantity

● aid in the management of grass by adjusting the area available for grazing.

This chapter examines the factors which influence the contribution that conserved forage can make to milk production. This requires a knowledge of the conservation process and the methods of assessing the quality of conserved forage. The role of conservation in overall grassland management is discussed in Chapter 4.

2.1 WINTER FEEDING – HAY OR SILAGE?

There is a continuing move away from hay towards silage making in the U.K. especially on dairy farms. There are several problems associated with hay-making. In addition to five or six days of dry weather, the following conditions aid the production of well-preserved, field-cured hay:-

● low yields to enable the swath to dry quickly

● stemmy crops to further aid drying

● little regrowth which might hinder drying.

These conditions are best met when low rates of fertilizer nitrogen are applied to produce a light crop which is cut at an advanced stage of maturity. The result is a low yield and a low feed value even before the crop is cut. Field curing of the hay further reduces feed value, especially in rainy conditions (Figure 2.1).

Figure 2.1   Effect of conservation system on the recovery of dry matter and relative feeding value.

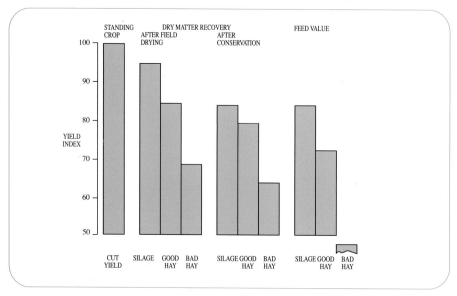

(Adapted from P. Lingvall, Swedish University of Agricultural Sciences)

Hay stubbles are slow to regrow and fertilizer applications are delayed while the crop is being tedded and baled. Thus, hay-making may not only fail to produce a good quality winter feed but also reduces the grass yield for the whole season and slow regrowth results in a shortage of grass for grazing in mid-season.

Hay-making is an inefficient way of using grass, and the cost of this is a greater need for bought-in feed. On most farms a move to silage making improves grassland utilisation and profitability.

2.2 SILAGE MAKING

(a) Silage Fermentation

The objective of silage making is to conserve forage quickly and cleanly with the minimum loss of feed value.

Grass is preserved when sugar is fermented into acid by bacteria. This is achieved when:-

- there is sufficient sugar in the grass (greater than 3% of fresh weight)
- air is excluded from the silo.

Good silage making is the result of rapid conversion of sugar to lactic acid.   Air in the

28

silo or lack of sugar in the grass results in the wrong type of fermentation.   Bacteria develop which break down lactic acid to weaker butyric acid and protein is converted into less valuable non-protein nitrogen.   Silage pH rises (Figure 2.2) and losses increase.

Figure 2.2   Pattern of silage pH in well and poorly preserved silages (18 to 20% dry matter).

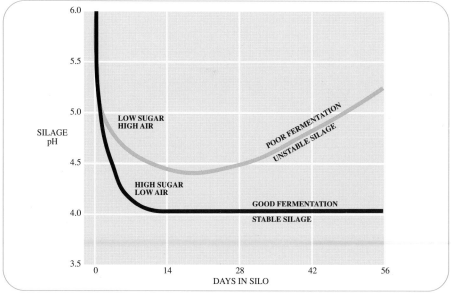

(R. F. Wilson, Grassland Research Institute)

(b) Factors Affecting the Fermentation of Silage

The major factors which affect the fermentation of silage are:

- ❑ species and varieties
- ❑ fertilizer applications
- ❑ stage of growth and timing of cuts
- ❑ wilting and control of effluent
- ❑ chop length
- ❑ additives
- ❑ silo filling
- ❑ feeding techniques
- ❑ contamination with soil and slurry

(i) *Species and Varieties*

Ryegrasses have high sugar contents and are the best choice for making into silage. Tetraploid varieties of ryegrass have higher sugar contents than diploids.   Legumes have

29

very low sugar and dry matter contents and also resist a fall in pH. Extra care needs to be taken when making silage from lucerne, red clover and grass/clover mixtures.

(ii) *Fertilizer Applications*

Fertilizer is essential to encourage high yields and it should be applied early for the grass to use it efficiently. One day's growth for each 2.5 kilograms of nitrogen should be allowed between fertilizer application and cutting. Guidance on this is given in Chapter 1, section 1.5. The rapid growth induced by high levels of fertilizer nitrogen results in a reduced sugar content; failure to use up all the fertilizer may produce a poor fermentation as a result of a high level of non-protein nitrogen in the crop.

(iii) Stage of Growth and Timing of Cuts

Grass feed value falls as the plant gets older and produces a seed head. However, early cuts of herbage can be more difficult to ensile than late cuts due to lower dry matter contents.

Sugar levels tend to be higher in the afternoon but the difference is small and should not influence the time of cutting. Grass should be cut as soon as dew or excessive surface water is off the plant to maximise the daylight hours available for drying the crop.

Season can also influence fermentation since sugar levels are lower in the autumn.

(iv) *Contamination with Soil and Slurry*

Contamination of silage with soil can occur if the cutting height of herbage is too low, particularly on uneven fields. Slurry can be a problem if it is applied too close to the time of cutting and should not be spread less than 8 weeks before cutting. Contamination leads to bad and uneven fermentation in the clamp and depressed feeding quality of the silage.

(v) *Wilting and Control of Effluent*

The objective of wilting is to remove some of the water from the crop. This has several advantages as it:-

● increases the concentration of sugar in the grass
● reduces the level of effluent (Figure 2.3a)
● reduces the activity of bacteria which cause poor fermentation
● speeds up handling of the silage during harvesting and feeding by reducing number of trailer loads needed (Figure 2.3 (b))
● reduces the size of the clamp which is required.

Figure 2.3 Effect of wilting on effluent production and trailer capacity.

(a) Effluent production.

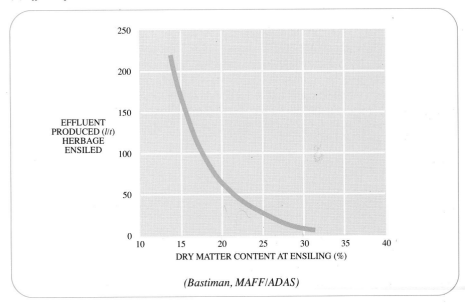

(Bastiman, MAFF/ADAS)

(b) Number of trailer loads per hectare of double chopped grass (assuming a yield of 5 tonnes of dry matter per hectare).

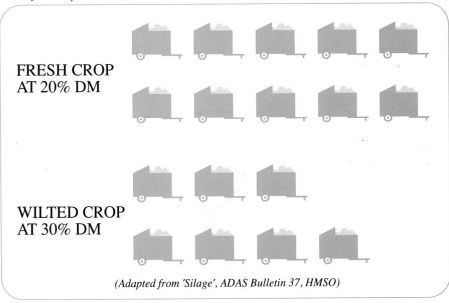

FRESH CROP
AT 20% DM

WILTED CROP
AT 30% DM

(Adapted from 'Silage', ADAS Bulletin 37, HMSO)

However,wilting increases the risk of field losses. Generally the increase in field loss is balanced by a reduction in within silo loss so that overall losses are little different between direct cut and wilted systems.

Wilting for a maximum 24 hours to a dry matter content of 25% achieves all of the benefits of better fermentation, little or no effluent and easier handling without the risk of high field losses. If dry matter contents of between 20 and 25% are consistently difficult to achieve then it may be worthwhile considering a mower conditioner with finger/brush elements to increase drying rate. In any event, even in the drier areas of the UK, the objective of 25% dry matter may not be achieved and it is vitally important that adequate facilities are available for the collection of effluent. This important problem is considered in more detail in section 2.3.

(vi) *Chop Length*

Chopping the crop during harvesting results in a quicker and more efficient fermentation since plant sap, containing sugars, is rapidly released. It also results in faster harvesting since more grass is carried in each trailer. In the clamp, short chop material is more easily compacted and therefore the silo contains less air. This effect is particularly valuable with dry herbage.

(vii) *Additives*

Additives act by:-

● supplying acid directly to the grass, e.g. sulphuric acid

● supplying acid directly and inhibiting some harmful bacteria, e.g. formic acid

● inhibiting all bacteria and preserving the silage, e.g. formalin or more recently high rates of formic or formic acid based additives

● supplying more sugars to the grass for the bacteria to convert into acid, e.g. molasses

● converting fibre into sugars by the use of enzymes

● supplying a source of efficient bacteria, e.g. inoculants.

Proprietary additives may operate in one of these ways (e.g. formic acid) or in two or more ways (e.g. acid/formalin mixtures or enzyme/inoculant combinations). Currently there are some 100 additives readily available for use in the UK. The most effective over a wide range of conditions are those based on formic acid.

Progress has been made in the provision of effective inoculants and some have resulted in considerable improvements in animal performance. However doubts remain as to their effectiveness in wet, low sugar or badly contaminated crops.

Enzymes in the form of cellulases and hemicellulases can release sugars and there is some limited evidence of improved animal performance, but as yet insufficient data are available to give a general recommendation. Amylases attack starches and are of little value in grasses.

Given the wide range of products on the market it is imperative that independent test results should be studied before buying an additive. These must show the effect of the additive on fermentation *and* on animal performance, when compared with the silage made without additive. Production data are particularly important where inoculants and enzymes are being considered since increases in milk yield have been observed even in the absence of changes in silage fermentation quality.

Additives remove a great deal of risk from silage making. A guide to the conditions when a silage additive will be beneficial is given in Table 2.1.

Table 2.1 Guide to additive use

	*****	****	***	**	*	Number of Stars
Species	Italian Ryegrass	Perennial Ryegrass or mainly Perennial Ryegrass	Non Ryegrass or Ryegrass/ White Clover	–	Legume	4
Fertilizer Nitrogen	–	–	Less than 50	50–100	More than 100 or legume	2
DM Content (%)	More than 25%	–	20–25%	–	Less than 20%	1
D Value (%)	–	Less than 60	60–65	More 65	–	2
Harvester	Precision	Double Chop	Flail	Forage Wagon	–	4
Season	–	–	Spring and Summer	–	Autumn	3
					Total	16

Total Stars	Risk of Poor Fermentation	Additive Use
Above 20	Low	Recommended rate for insurance only
15–20	Medium	Recommended rate
Below 15	High	Consult maker for high rate of addition

In the example (page 33) perennial ryegrass (****) which received 80 kg of fertilizer N/ha (50-100, **) had a DM content of 18% (less than 20%, *) a D-value of 68 (more than 65, **) and was harvested with a double chop machine (****) in spring (***). The total number of stars is 16 and, by consulting the table, this shows that the crop needs additive applied at the recommended rate.

Alternatively, the sugar content of the herbage can be used to assess the need for an additive. Sugar contents of less than 3% of fresh weight will mean that additive is required. At a very low level of sugar content (less than 2%) a high rate of additive will be needed to ensure a good fermentation.

Herbage from swards containing a significant quantity of clover will be of lower dry matter and sugar content than material from grass only swards, and will always require an additive under most UK conditions if reliable quality silage is to be made.

(viii) *Silo Filling*

Silos should be filled:-

- ❏ **quickly**, to reduce the time that grass is exposed to air
- ❏ **evenly**, to achieve uniform consolidation
- ❏ **cleanly**, to minimise soil contamination.

The Dorset Wedge system of filling provides the most efficient method of excluding air (Figure 2.4). The silage should be sheeted at night; otherwise air in the silo will heat up, rise and draw in more air. As soon as the clamp is finished it should be sealed with polythene sheets, weighted down and the sheet protected. Side sheets are important so that the top sheet can overlap those on the shoulders where waste is most likely to occur.

If the clamp is re-opened for subsequent cuts disturbance of the existing top layer should be minimised.

Figure 2.4 Dorset wedge filling technique

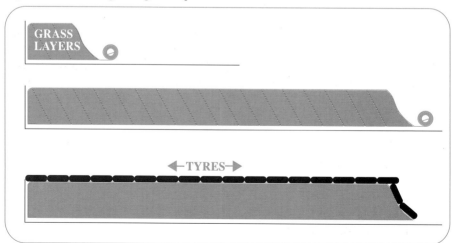

(ix) *Feeding Techniques*

Silage will remain in good condition for many years if the clamp is sealed. The silo can be opened three to four weeks from final sealing but deterioration starts if the silage face is left open and exposed for too long.

To minimise deterioration:-

❑ silage at the face should be removed at an average rate of at least 10 cm/day in cold weather and 30 cm/day in warm weather.
❑ the face should be disturbed as little as possible; where possible a block cutter or shear grab should be used rather than a foreloader.

(c) Big Bale Silage

Big bale silage is an invaluable aid to grassland management on the dairy farm when small quantities of silage need to be made at times outside the main cuts or when existing clamps are full. The advantages are:-

❑ no need to open clamp
❑ low labour and machinery requirements
❑ suitable for contractor operation.

However, good big bale silage requires care and attention not only in the making but also in handling and feeding. The key to making good quality baled silage is:-

❑ avoid soil contamination. Cutting height should be at least 5 cm
❑ round balers work best with longer material
❑ produce a swath to match baler width
❑ wilt to 25-35% dry matter if possible (do not use wrappers for herbage of less than 25% dry matter to avoid effluent)
❑ drive slowly to get high bale density
❑ prepare a proper storage site away from vermin
❑ ensure tight seal with bags and for wrapping use 50% overlap 2+2 system and good quality plastic
❑ take care in handling, storing and removing bales from the stack to avoid damage
❑ minimise losses at feeding by using an appropriate feeder.

Wrapping is becoming increasingly popular. It has advantages over bagging:-

❑ less labour
❑ less wastage
❑ copes with variable bale size
but,
❑ higher machinery costs/contractors required
❑ less suitable for wet material
❑ more care needed in stacking

2.3 EFFLUENT CONTROL

(a) Pollution

Silage effluent is a very potent pollutant. Effluent consists of plant juices which provide an excellent food source for micro-organisms in water courses. These develop rapidly and remove a considerable amount of oxygen from the water, thus causing the death of fish and plant life in rivers, streams and ponds. The quantity of oxygen used by the micro-organisms is called the 5-day Biochemical or Biological Oxygen Demand (BOD). Silage effluent can have a BOD of 80,000 compared with a typical value for raw sewage of around 300. Hence, the polluting power of silage effluent from only a 300t clamp is equivalent to the sewage produced daily by the population of a large town.

(b) Collection

The volume of effluent depends on the type and stage of maturity of the crop, the quality of material to be ensiled and most importantly its dry matter content. Table 2.2 provides a guide to the quantities of effluent that will need to be collected.

Table 2.2 A guide to expected effluent production.

Silage dry matter %	Effluent produced (m³/100t)	
	Total	Maximum daily rate
15	33	3.3
20	22	2.2
25	11	1.1

Site construction and effluent collection facilities must comply with the law and the codes of good agricultural practice. Effective collection requires a well constructed, watertight floor and drainage facilities to direct effluent into a tank. The size of tank must be sufficient to cope with the maximum flow rate since about half of effluent volume in Table 2.2 will be produced during the first week after grass is deposited in the clamp.

Guidance on silo construction and collection systems should be obtained from the advisory services and any new construction should be discussed with the appropriate river authority.

(c) Disposal

Effluent can be disposed of by spreading a 1:1 mixture with water at the rate of 20 m³/ha. At these rates effluent should supply 12 kg N, 6 kg P_2O_5 and 40 kg K_2O per hectare. Alternatively effluent can be fed to cattle and cows will consume 15-20 litres/day, equivalent in feeding value to 0.7 to 0.8 kg of barley/day. The value of effluent (1988 prices) has been estimated at £0.48 per 1000 litres as a fertilizer and at £6.33 per 1000 litres as a feed.

(d) Absorbents

Materials can be added to grass before ensilage to absorb effluent, thus reducing or even eliminating effluent loss. Absorbents are useful where the dry matter of herbage for ensilage is habitually low and/or the cost of implementing other means of effective effluent control is prohibitive. An ideal absorbent should:-

❑ have a high moisture holding capacity under load
❑ be resistant to degradation in the clamp
❑ improve silage digestibility and feeding value
❑ have a high density
❑ contain little or no soluble materials
❑ be cheap and readily available during the silage making season

The relative absorbency of some commonly used materials are shown in Table 2.3. Fibrous materials have greater absorbency than cereal grains.

A bottom layer of straw bales in the clamp actually increases silage effluent loss and should never be used.

The inclusion rate of absorbent is very important. 75 Kg fresh weight of chopped straw or molassed beet shreds per tonne of grass fresh weight may eliminate effluent loss, but increases the volume needed to store a given tonnage by 80% (chopped straw) and 20% (molassed beet shreds).

Table 2.3 Relative absorbency of materials for grass silage

Material	Relative absorbency
Chopped barley straw	100
Dried distillers grains	66
Molassed beet shreds	60
Alkali treated straw cubes	53
Molassed beet nuts	49
Rolled barley	16

While chopped straw will reduce silage feeding value, molassed beet shreds will increase it and aid fermentation. However, molassed beet shreds will increase the pollutant power (BOD) of effluent produced and costs more per tonne than chopped straw. Therefore, if molassed beet shreds are to be used they should be added at a rate which will eliminate effluent loss. The amount required can be calculated using the following equation:

Molassed beet shreds = 419 - (19.1 X Grass dry matter %)
(Kg fresh weight/t grass fresh weight)

37

Thus, for a tonne of fresh grass at a dry matter content of 15%, 133 Kg of molassed beet shreds are required to eliminate effluent loss. At 20% dry matter, 37 Kg molassed beet shreds are needed.

Clearly, there are no 'ideal' absorbents available at present. When absorbents are necessary the local advisory services should be consulted. It is also important to remember that the dry matter content of grass for ensilage can vary widely within and between seasons, which means that absorbents will never replace good clamp design and storage facilities for handling large quantities of effluent.

2.4 FEEDING OF SILAGE

(a) Assessment of Silage Quality

The value of silage depends on the fermentation quality and the energy and protein value of the silage.

For analysis of silage it is essential to ensure the material analysed is representative of the silage in the whole clamp.

In this section the items on a silage analysis form (Table 2.4) are explained.

Table 2.4 Analysis form

Farmer's Name: ....
Address: ....
....
....

Date: ....

	Sample Details	Reference
	Dry Matter (DM) content (%)	(i)
Fermentation Quality	pH	(ii)
	Ammonia nitrogen (% of total nitrogen)	
	Total Ash (%)	
Energy Value	MAD Fibre/OMD (%)	(iii)
	D-value (%)	
	•ME value (MJ/Kg DM)	
Protein Value	Crude Protein (%)	(iv)
	**RDP (g/Kg DM) UDP (g/Kg DM)	

* ME   –   Metabolisable Energy expressed in Megajoules per Kg of Dry matter (MJ/Kg DM)
** RDP – Rumen degradable protein in g per Kg dry matter (g/Kg DM = % x 10)
  UDP   – Undegradable protein in g per Kg dry matter (g/Kg DM = % x 10)

(i) *Dry Matter Content*

This is the percentage of dry matter in the total wet silage. The remainder is water. All feed rationing should be done on a dry matter basis.

The normal oven drying method for measuring dry matter content is unsuitable for silage since many of the fermentation products are lost. A 'true' dry matter content, which includes these important constituents, must be used.

(ii) *Fermentation Quality Measures*

pH

pH is a measure of acidity. The lower the pH, the more acid and better preserved is the silage. The wetter the silage the lower will be the pH required for good preservation. A broad guide to quality in relation to dry matter content and pH is given in Figure 2.5.

Figure 2.5 Fermentation quality in relation to silage pH and dry matter content.

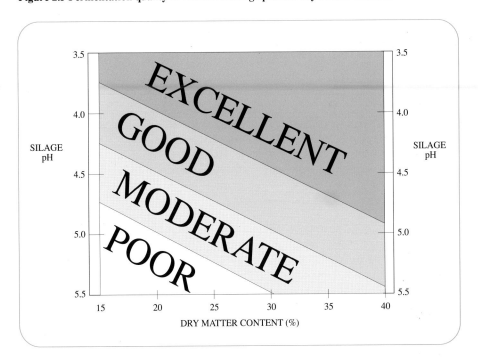

Ammonia Nitrogen

The ammonia nitrogen content of the silage is often expressed as a percentage of total nitrogen and gives a guide to the amount of protein breakdown that has occurred during fermentation. It is also the best single indicator of silage fermentation quality (Table 2.5).

Table 2.5 Ammonia nitrogen content as a guide to fermentation quality.

Quality of Fermentation	Ammonia Nitrogen (% of total nitrogen)
Excellent	Below 5%
Good	5-10%
Moderate	10-15%
Poor	Above 15%

Total Ash

This is the mineral content of the silage. Ash values greater than 10% usually indicate soil contamination which causes poor fermentation and results in a low intake of silage. A high content of ash also dilutes the energy value of the silage.

(iii) *Energy Value*

MAD Fibre
Modified Acid Detergent (MAD) fibre is a convenient and rapid measure of the fibre content of the silage. The less mature the grass the lower is the MAD fibre content and higher is the feed energy value of the silage. However, the relationship between MAD fibre and energy value is poor and this method is no longer used in the UK for routine silage analysis.

D-value
D-value is the standard measure used to describe the digestibility of herbage and silage. It is measured by incubating a sample of the silage with rumen liquour followed by enzymes. The less mature the grass the higher will be the D-value and feed energy value of the silage.

Metabolisable Energy (ME)
The Metabolisable Energy (ME) system is now the standard system used to ration dairy cows. The ME value expressed as Megajoules per kg of dry matter (MJ/kg DM) is the measure of the feed energy value of the silage. It can be estimated from the MAD fibre content (or less commonly, D-value and crude protein) of the silage. More recently SAC, ADAS and DANI have converted to the much more accurate system based on 'near infrared reflectance' (NIR). This new technology of NIR predicts the organic matter digestibility (OMD) of grass silage. This is then used to calculate the energy value. The higher the OMD, the higher the energy value. NIR provides a more accurate and reliable

estimation of energy value than MAD fibre. The accuracy of NIR is shown in Figure 2.6, where OMD predicted by NIR is plotted against OMD measured in ruminants and the error of prediction in this method is now down to about 0.3 MJ/kg dry matter. A full explanation of the ME system is given in MAFF, Reference Book 433, 'Energy Allowances and Feeding Systems for Ruminants', (HMSO, London, 1985).

Figure 2.6 Relationship between OMD predicted by NIR and actual OMD for grass silages.

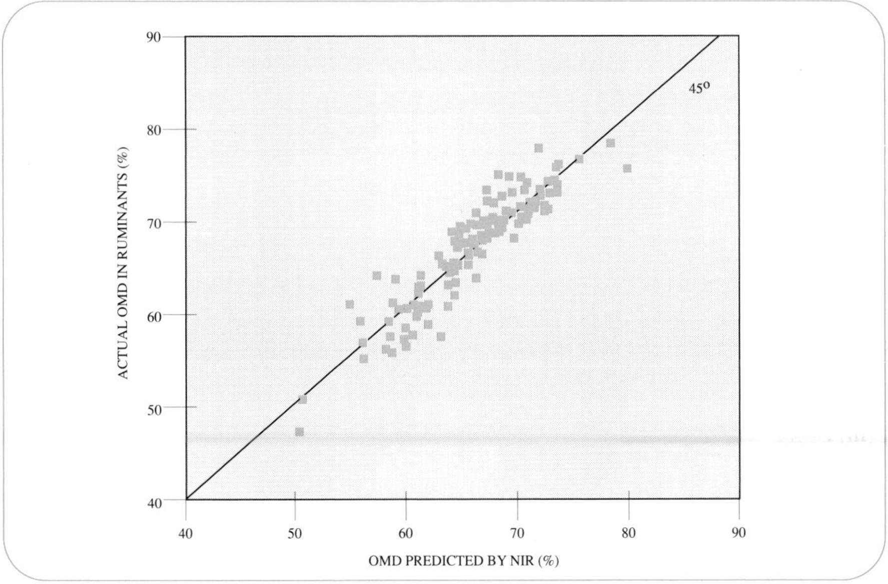

(M.S.F. Kridis, SAC)

(iv) *Protein Value*

Crude Protein (CP)
This is a measure of the total nitrogen in the silage and implies, wrongly, that all of the nitrogen is in the form of protein.

Digestible Crude Protein (DCP)
Digestible Crude Protein was for many years the standard measure of the protein value of silages. It is calculated from the crude protein content. The DCP system does not take into account the fact that the availability of protein to the cow is different in different feeds. For instance the amount of protein supplied by dried grass is likely to be higher than that from silage, even if the DCP content of the forages is the same.

(v) *A New Protein System*

A new protein system has been developed to overcome the deficiencies of DCP. This system separates protein into two forms:

Rumen Degradable Protein (RDP)

This contains the non-protein nitrogen and the portion of protein which is broken down in the rumen and used by micro-organisms. The micro-organisms are then digested in the small intestine and the protein used by the dairy cow. The amount of rumen degradable protein that can be used by the micro-organisms depends on the ME value of the diet.

Too little RDP results in a fall in the amount of fibre digested in the rumen and a fall in intake. An excess of RDP in relation to the ME value of the diet results in a wastage of protein.

Undegradable Protein (UDP)

This is the portion of protein which is not broken down in the rumen and passes through to the small intestine to be directly available to the cow. The amount of UDP required by the cow depends on the difference between the protein required for production and that supplied by RDP.

Many modifications have been made to the original system. The most important are:-

- RDP is now split into quickly and slowly degradable fractions. This will take into account, for example, that silages can contain considerable amounts of very soluble nitrogen which is not used efficiently.

- The efficiency with which microbes work is greater in lactating cows with their high intakes than in dry cows fed only to maintain their condition.

- UDP varies in its value. For example, heat treatments and conservation methods can reduce the availability of UDP for milk production.

These modifications mean that the minimum crude protein for high producing cows is now in excess of 16% CP in the diet, which is much more in line with results from feeding trials.

The new protein system enables the dairy cow to be fed the best balance of RDP and UDP.

(b) Achieving the Potential of Silage for Milk Production

The value of silage for milk production depends on the quantity of silage eaten by the cow and the energy and protein value of that silage. In turn, these factors are influenced by the amount offered, the method of feeding the silage, its fermentation quality, digestibility and the amount of concentrates fed.

An example of silage as a sole feed for cows is shown in Table 2.6. Cows and heifers ate 11.5-13.5 Kg of silage dry matter per day, ranging in ME content from 10.6 to 11.5 MJ. This resulted in good yields and apart from low ME silages, in good milk quality. The cows were turned out to grass, again with no concentrate. Lactation yields averaged between 4430 and 4950 litres per cow.

Table 2.6 Performance of January/February calving Friesian X Holstein cows offered silage as a sole feed and grazed with no concentrate supplementation.

	Heifers	Cows
No. of animals	10	63
Silage DM (%)	21-36	
Silage ME (MJ/Kg DM)	10.6-11.5	
Silage intake (Kg DM/day)	11.5-13.6	
Milk yield (Kg/day)	15.7-16.1	19.4-23.1
Lactation yield (Kg)	3922-4138	4430-4949
Milk composition (g/Kg):		
Fat	36.2-40.7	
Protein	27.2-31.8	

(R.C. Rae, ICI)

The objective of this section is to outline the principles of feeding silage rather than to define rations for dairy cows.

(i) *Method of Feeding*

The need to feed silage to appetite is essential for efficient milk production. *Ad libitum* feeding, that is silage available at all times, is not common and restriction of silage is a major cause of reduced milk yields.

There must also be sufficient space for each cow at the trough or silo:

Trough feeding
❑ silage available for 24 hours each day
❑ a minimum of 15 cm of trough space per cow

Self feeding
❑ a minimum of 20 cm of face per cow
❑ face height less than 2.0 m.

A guide to the quantities of silage required for *ad libitum* access is shown in Figure 2.7 and in more detail in Appendix 2.1.

Figure 2.7 Target silage requirement (tonnes of dry matter) and minimum concentrate inputs (tonnes, as fed) for a 180 day winter (herd yield 5500-6000 litres).

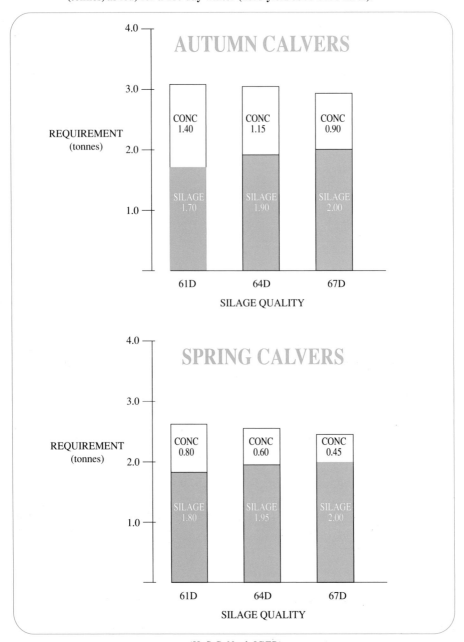

(H. StC. Neal, IGER)

(ii) *Fermentation Quality*

Effect on silage intake
Cows can eat 13 to 14 kg of dry matter per day when they are given silage of high quality as the sole feed. However, a poor fermentation results in a loss of feed value in the silage. It also results in the cow eating less and therefore giving even lower milk yields. The ammonia nitrogen content of the silage is often a good indicator of likely silage intake (Table 2.7).

Table 2.7 The relationship between ammonia nitrogen content and relative intake of silage.

Ammonia Nitrogen as % of Total Nitrogen	Relative Intake
Less than 5%	100
5-10%	98
10-15%	95
More than 15%	90

Poor fermentation can result in a major reduction in silage intake. For example, the intake of high pH silages (above pH 4.2) can be very low and this is often associated with high ammonia nitrogen and low lactic acid contents. Silage intake can also be depressed if the pH is very low (below pH 3.3). Every effort must be made by following the rules on pages 28 – 35 to achieve a good fermentation.

Wilting
Wilting does not result in higher milk yields (Figure 2.8) provided wet silage can be well preserved. On the other hand, the use of effective additives such as formic acid on wet herbage improves fermentation, silage intake and milk yield (Figure 2.9).

However, wilting reduces effluent production and speeds harvesting and these managerial advantages outweigh any nutritional disadvantages provided the field period is short and drying is rapid. Further, machinery travel should be minimised to reduce the effect of wheel damage which can have a considerable affect on yield of grass for subsequent cuts.

The aim should be:

to wilt for 24 hours with the objective of reaching 25% dry matter

Table 2.1 should be consulted for additive application and a higher rate may be necessary if 25% dry matter is not achieved.

Figure 2.8 The effect of wilting on milk yield.

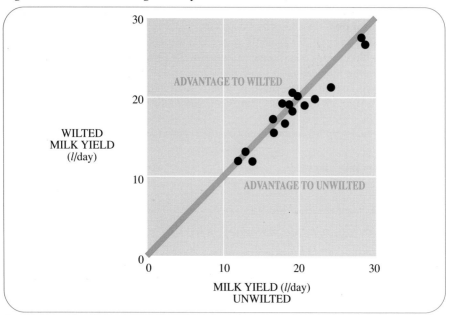

Figure 2.9 The effect of silage additive on milk yield.

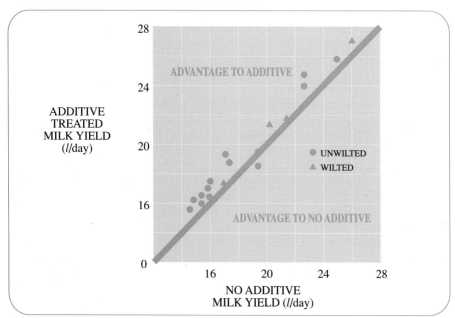

Chop Length

Short chopping can increase silage intake and milk yield over and above that which would be expected from the improvements in fermentation. This is because short particles of silage break down more rapidly in the rumen than long particles. The effect is likely to be greater with low digestibility silage (less than 64/65 D-value) and with low levels of concentrate.

There is little evidence that the chop length produced by precision-chop harvesters affects milk fat.

(iii) *Digestibility*

Cutting grass earlier and more frequently results in a silage of low fibre content and higher digestibility. This means higher intakes and more milk.

An increase in silage D-value of 1 unit increases:-

❑ silage intake by 0.15 kg of dry matter/cow per day

❑ milk yield by 0.30 l/cow per day.

The effect is likely to be less when high levels of concentrate are fed, since silage is a lower proportion of the total diet.

Good fermentation is necessary in order to achieve these increases and the likely saving in concentrates under these conditions is shown in Figure 2.7 on page 44.

Choosing the optimum silage quality for the individual farm has important effects on grassland utilisation and on profitability. This is discussed in more detail in Chapter 4.

(iv) *Grass/Clover Silage*

Silage made from mixed swards of ryegrass and white clover can have higher protein, energy and minerals contents compared to silage made from ryegrass only swards. Feeding grass/clover silage to lactating cows can also give improved milk yield and composition. A typical comparison of feeding value for grass/clover and grass silages is shown in Table 2.8.

The improved feeding value of silage gained by using mixed swards is only consistently obtained if the proportion of clover in the dry matter of cut herbage is greater then 20%. Recommendations for managing mixed swards to obtain this quantity of clover can be found in Chapter 1.

It should be remembered that the small increases in milk yield and composition achieved by feeding grass/clover silage are dependant on good silage making and feeding techniques. Obtaining a good fermentation with grass/clover herbage in the silo can be more difficult than with grass alone, due to the lower dry matter and sugar content of clover. In addition, benefits will only be seen where silage is fed to appetite.

Table 2.8 The average feeding value of grass and grass/clover silages (3-cut system) over 2 years (1986/87).

	Grass/white clover silage	Grass silage
Dry matter (%)	14.6	16.6
ME (MJ/Kg DM)	11.0	10.9
CP (g/Kg DM)	164	144
D-Value	71.8	70.7
Minerals (g/Kg DM)		
Calcium	9.9	5.5
Phosphorous	3.9	3.4
Magnesium	2.4	2.3
Potassium	25.3	18.0

(D. J. Roberts, SAC)

(v) *Concentrate*

Amount of concentrate

When cows which have been given silage to appetite are fed additional concentrate they eat less silage. This fall in silage intake, known as substitution, is greater with high quality silage and is also greater at high levels of concentrate input.

With good quality silage (above 65 D-value and less than 10% ammonia-N) and with more than 8 kg of concentrate per day, the substitution of silage by extra concentrate is very high; little increase in total energy intake is seen and the extra milk from feeding the extra concentrate can be very disappointing.

Another reason for a disappointing response is that more energy is put into live weight gain and less into milk as concentrate input is increased.

The effect of concentrate on lactation yield in a herd given good quality silage to appetite is shown in Table 2.9.

Lactation yield increased up to 1.1t of concentrate/cow and then remained relatively constant, at about 5700 to 5800 l. Even below 1.1t the cow required 0.8 kg of concentrate to produce an extra litre of milk, nearly double the standard 0.4 to 0.5 kg/l (4 to 5 lb/gal).

Table 2.9 The response in milk yield to increased concentrate use.

Concentrate fed (t/cow)	0.6	0.9	1.1	1.4	1.6
Lactation yield (t/cow)	5140	5420	5760	5680	5810

(F.J. Gordon, Hillsborough)

Minimum concentrate input and target silage requirements

The contribution that well-preserved silage can make to milk production depends on its quality. Less concentrate is needed to achieve a given milk yield as silage digestibility rises with increased cutting frequency. This is shown in Figure 2.7 which also gives a guide to the target silage requirements for *ad libitum* access and minimum winter concentrate needed to achieve a yield of 5500 l.

It is worth noting that spring calvers require almost the same quantity of silage as autumn calvers. A detailed table of requirement can be found in Appendix 2.1.

An example of the influence of these various combinations of silage and concentrate on land required for conservation is shown in Figure 2.10. It can be seen that more land is required to be closed up for conservation, particularly for the first cut, as grass growing conditions worsen (site classes 1 to 5). More detailed tables of areas to be closed up for conservation are presented in Appendix 2.2.

Pattern of Distribution

Treating cows as individuals, and feeding relatively more concentrate in early lactation is thought to be important in achieving high milk yields and in using concentrates efficiently. This is true where either of the following apply:-

● forage is of low quality
● forage is in short supply and is being restricted.

However, if forage is of good quality (more than 64 D-value (10.2 MJ of ME/kg DM) and less than 10% ammonia-N) and is fed to appetite, a simple 'flat rate' or 'step rate' feeding system is as good as any other. This means feeding all cows the same rate after they have calved either for most of the winter or in two steps. Lactation yield depends more on the total amount of concentrates fed per cow, rather than the way in which it is allocated. Thus, making good quality silage in sufficient quantities to ensure *ad libitum* access can simplify the management of the herd.

(vi) Type of Concentrate

Fibre

Compound feeds now contain less grain and more fibrous by-products. Concentrates high in good quality fibre can overcome milk fat depression at high concentrate levels. However, at concentrate inputs of 5-8 Kg/day there is little difference between starchy and fibrous compounds in their ability to produce milk fat and protein. When feeding low levels of concentrate (less than 3 Kg/day) the use of barley or wheat in the concentrate can improve both fat and protein.

Fat

Good quality protected fat can increase yields and milk fat content. However, milk protein content tends to fall. Great care should be taken in choosing a high fat compound or straight and independent advice should be sought.

Figure 2.10 Areas required for conservation (ha/cow) for autumn calvers yielding 6000 litres (for definition of site classes see Chapter 1, Table 1.2).

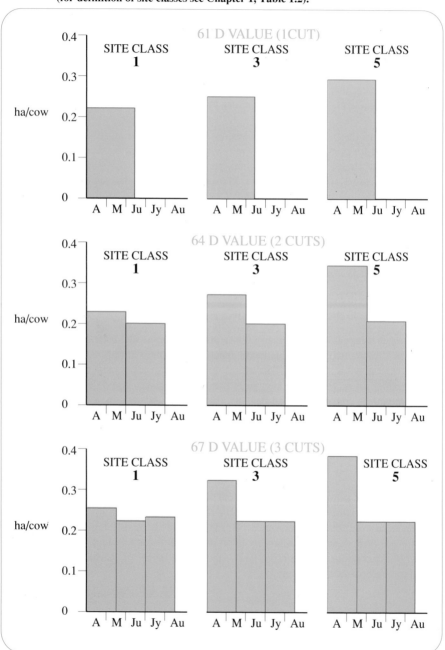

Protein

Silage is a poor source of protein and worthwhile increases in milk yield can be obtained by using higher protein concentrates. Normally 18 to 20% crude protein in the concentrate should be appropriate.

Recent work has shown that small quantities (around 3 Kg/day) of concentrates containing 35 to 45% crude protein provide a good compliment to high digestibility silage. Using this system lactation yields of 5200 to 5900 litres have been obtained with autumn and spring calving herds. However, the system requires at least 12 tonnes (2.4 t DM) of silage made per cow.

2.4 CONCLUSIONS

The key to efficient conservation is the preservation of herbage with a minimum loss of quantity and quality. Silage making is less weather dependent than hay making and therefore has the potential to incur lower losses during conservation. Low losses in silage making and feeding can be achieved by following the rules set out below.

Summary of rules for efficient silage making

- Aim at medium to high digestibility (65 to 70 D-value).
- Wilt for 24 hours to achieve 25% dry matter if possible.
- Harvest the crop cleanly (minimum soil contamination).
- Chop or lacerate.
- Apply effective additives according to guidelines.
- Ensile rapidly and cleanly.
- Compact each layer.
- Cover the silo overnight.
- Seal the silo well and immediately weigh down top sheet.
- Reduce disturbance of the silo face.
- Remove face by at least 10 cm/day in cold weather, 30 cm/day in warm weather.

Reducing losses of dry matter in silage making from, say, 30 to 20% allows a saving in conservation of about 0.5 t/cow. Such reductions in losses are achievable and should be considered as an important method for increasing profitability.

Restrictions on the uncontrolled loss of silage effluent into water courses have increased and are likely to become more stringent. Great care must be taken in silo design and construction to eliminate pollution by effluent.

High milk yields can be obtained from silage supplemented with only low amounts of concentrates provided the silage is well preserved, is of high quality and is offered to appetite *(ad libitum)*. Utilisation of grassland can only be maximised if an efficient conservation system is combined with a complementary feeding strategy.

CHAPTER 3

GRAZING

Sinclair Mayne, Alan Reeve and Martin Hutchinson

3.1 Grass production under grazing
3.2 Potential of grazed grass for milk production
3.3 Guidelines for grazing management
3.4 Choice of grazing system
3.5 Role of concentrates and other supplementary feeds
3.6 Conclusions

Grazed grass is the cheapest feed for dairy cows and, as a sole feed, is capable of sustaining high individual animal performance. Similar levels of milk production can be obtained from both short term leys and good permanent pasture when appropriately managed. Furthermore, the season's grazing strategy and its actual achievement largely dictates the success of the whole dairy system. Achieving efficient utilization from the grazed area means that a balance between yield per cow and yield per hectare must be achieved and maintained throughout the grazing season. The aim of this chapter is to outline some of the factors, such as stocking rate and sward height, which enable this balance to be achieved. Guidelines are given for different site classes in terms of target stocking rates and sward heights through the season.

3.1 GRASS PRODUCTION UNDER GRAZING

Grass growth is usually estimated by cutting and weighing grass from small plots from which grazing animals are excluded. However, estimates of grass growth obtained under these conditions are of limited value in calculating grass growth under continuous grazing, where grass is being eaten almost as quickly as it grows.

Grass will grow best when there is a full ground cover of leaves to capture all the available light. Unfortunately, the total amount of grass consumed over the season by cattle grazing this type of sward is low. This is demonstrated in Figure 3.1. This occurs because a high proportion of the grass produced in a tall sward dies unharvested. For example, when more than 3 leaves appear on a perennial ryegrass tiller (about once every 11 days from April to September), the oldest leaf on that tiller dies. With tightly grazed swards:-

Less grass is produced
but
A much higher proportion is eaten before it dies.

Although the leaf area of a sward cannot be easily assessed at farm level, it has been shown that measurements of sward height can be used to define the best balance between grass production and the total amount consumed per ha over the season.

Figure 3.1 Effect of severity of grazing on grass production, intake and loss.

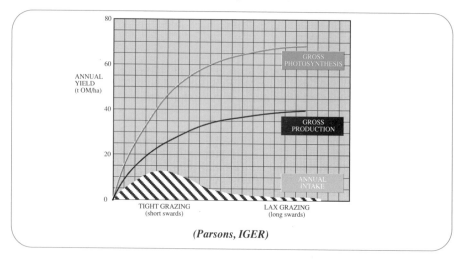

(Parsons, IGER)

In swards cut at monthly intervals there is a peak of herbage growth in May-June (see Figure 1.4) when grass shoots become reproductive and stem development increases. Cutting removes these shoots resulting in a greater proportion of tillers present in the vegetative state and hence subsequent growth is depressed. By contrast, in swards continuously grazed, elongating shoots are eaten off at a much earlier stage of development and new vegetative tillers continue to be produced. The seasonal pattern of production under continuous grazing is thus more uniform than under cutting, as illustrated in Figure 1.4. Under rotational grazing more frequent defoliation than under cutting reduces the extent of reproductive development, although the seasonal pattern of growth still tends to reflect that observed under cutting.

3.2 POTENTIAL OF GRAZED GRASS FOR MILK PRODUCTION

In terms of nutritive value, numerous studies have shown that grazed grass can support milk yields up to 27 litres per cow per day under good early season grazing conditions. The milk yields that can be supported from grass alone through the grazing season are shown in Figure 3.2. Results from other studies suggest that under certain conditions even higher milk yields may be obtained with swards containing a high proportion of white clover. For example, under experimental conditions:-

Cows grazing pure white clover swards produced up to **10% more milk** per day than those on ryegrass swards.

However, this may not be the case for mixed grass/white clover pastures. More recent evidence suggests that in practice milk production from well managed grass swards is equivalent to that produced from mixed grass/white clover swards. Furthermore, grass/white clover swards will produce lower dry matter yields than those obtained from well fertilized pure grass swards. For example, a reduction in stocking rate of approximately 25% would be required with a grass/clover system. Grass/clover swards are also associated with:-

- Low year to year reliability
- Poor spring growth
- Increased risk of bloat, particularly where high clover contents are obtained

Figure 3.2 Potential daily milk production for *ad libitum* high quality grazing.

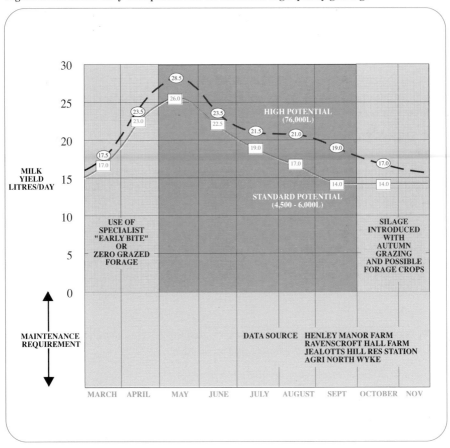

Where farm conditions permit, the grazing season can be extended by the use of early grazing varieties of rye or Italian ryegrass in the spring and by the use of silage and/or other forage crops for the autumn period.

(a) Effect of Diet Composition and Nutrition Pre-turnout

Cows fed diets containing a high proportion of high quality silage prior to turnout can produce higher milk yields when grazing than animals previously fed on high-concentrate diets. This effect may result from avoidance of the rapid changes in rumen fermentation pattern associated with a change from a high-concentrate to a high-forage diet following turnout, and through effects on appetite control. Such effects are obviously much more important with late-winter or spring calving cows than with autumn-calving cows. However, in all cases it is important to introduce cows gradually to grazing in the spring particularly if high levels of concentrates have been fed during the winter period.

(b) Efficient Utilization of Grass

A fundamental problem facing dairy farmers is that, in order to achieve milk yields of the order shown in Figure 3.2 only about half of the grass crop is consumed at any one grazing. The amount of grass utilized under grazing is influenced mainly by stocking rate which must be matched to:

- the grass growing conditions (site class, Chapter 1)
- the levels of N, P and K applied
- cutting strategy
- stage of lactation
- expected milk yield

Efficient use of grass requires high stocking rates and, as the competition between animals increases, milk yields decline as indicated in Figure 3.3. Two main observations can be made:

- maximum yield per hectare is achieved at a stocking rate which depresses yield per cow
- maximum yield per cow is only achieved at stocking rates substantially below those required to maximise milk yield per hectare.

An example of these effects is given in Table 3.1.

In the example from rotational grazing, increasing the grazing stocking rate from 4.4 to 5.9 cows/ha resulted in a reduction in sward height after grazing from 9.7 to 7.7 cm. Cows on the high stocking rate produced:

10% less milk than those on the low stocking rate
but
milk production per ha was 21% greater on the high stocking rate;

Figure 3.3 Effect of stocking rate on milk output per cow and per hectare. (Site class 2, 250 kg nitrogen/ha).

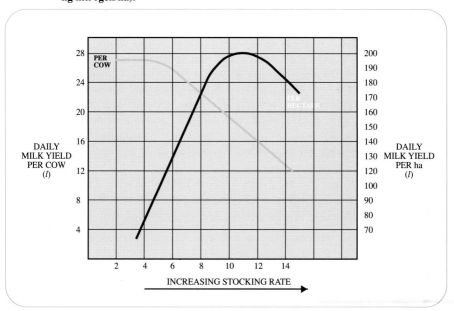

Grazing swards more tightly enabled an increase in the quantity of herbage consumed/ha relative to that on the low stocking rate. The key to efficient grassland management lies in the skill of the grazier to achieve a compromise between individual animal performance and milk output per hectare.

Table 3.1 Effect of stocking rate on solids corrected milk yield during the grazing season.

	Stocking rate (Grazing only, cows/ha)		Difference (%)
Rotational grazing	4.4	5.9	+34
Sward height after grazing (cm)	9.7	7.7	-21
Yield per cow (kg/day)	18	16	-10
Yield per ha (kg/day)	79	95	+21
	(Reeve, ICI)		
Continuous grazing	4.0	5.1	+28
Sward height (cm)	9.2	6.4	-30
Yield per cow (Kg/day)	20.4	18.6	- 9
Yield per ha (Kg/day)	82	94	+15
	(Fisher, SAC)		

(c) Grass quality

The digestibility (D-value) of the grass consumed from a well managed sward follows a characteristic pattern through the season (Figure 3.4).   By ensuring that the sward is well managed it is possible to offer young leafy herbage of high digestibility (more than 68 D-value) to the cows at all times.   Failure to graze the sward tightly in early season results in stem development, leading to a lower proportion of leaf in the sward in mid and late season.   This effect is illustrated in Figure 3.5 where the sward structure of rotationally grazed swards grazed to either 6.5, 8 or 12 cm was determined both in early June and again in mid-July.   The results indicate that whilst all swards were very leafy in early June:

- ● **undergrazing (lax grazing) in early season resulted in a marked increase in stem content of sward in mid July.**

Consequently, milk production from this sward was considerably depressed (up to 5 litres/cow/day) compared to the swards which were well grazed in early season.

Figure 3.4 D-value of herbage eaten by cows on a well managed grazing system.

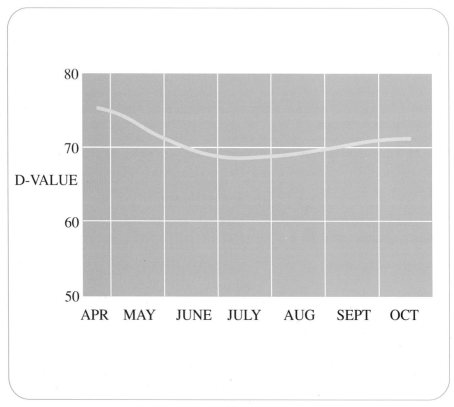

Figure 3.5 Effect of undergrazing in early season on sward structure.

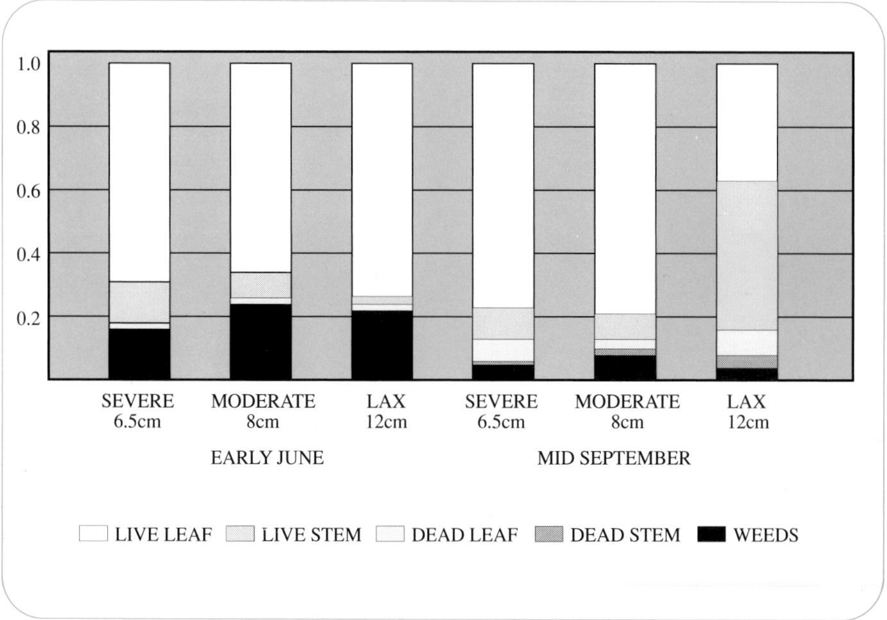

These effects are particularly important with cows calving from the middle of May to late August, where low sward quality in mid and late season could result in a marked depression of milk yield. However, as most of these animals are dry at some time from May to June, tight stocking in the spring can be practiced enabling maintenance of high sward quality throughout the season.

3.3 GUIDELINES FOR GRAZING MANAGEMENT

(a) Sward height

Grass growth fluctuates markedly both between and within seasons and in such circumstances mean stocking rates are of little value for day to day control over grazing management. A much more effective means of monitoring the supply of grass available to the dairy cow involves measuring sward surface height, either with a ruler, a graduated walking stick or with a "sward stick" comprising a central graduated rod with a sliding plastic tongue which is lowered until contact is made with green leaf.

At least 20 measurements of sward height should be taken at random from grazed and rejected areas but avoiding gateways and areas around troughs and trees.

Figure 3.6 **Effect of sward height after grazing on herbage intake and milk yield (rotational grazing).**

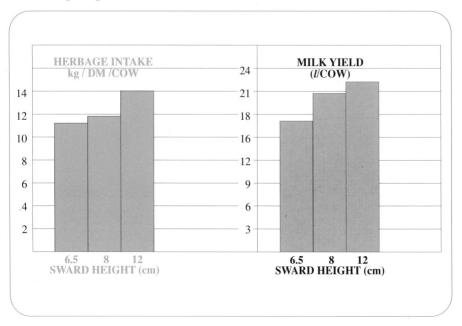

As the sward is grazed closer to the ground, both herbage intake and milk yield/cow are progressively reduced as shown in Figure 3.6. In practice, measurements of sward height can be used in both rotational and continuous grazing systems with heights being based on:

● the average stubble heights after grazing in rotational systems
● the average height of the sward maintained under continuous grazing.

Under rotational grazing a reasonable compromise between yield per cow and yield per ha can be achieved by grazing swards down to 8-10 cm (Figure 3.7) whilst under continuous grazing, swards should be grazed down to 6-8 cm (Figure 3.8). Swards can be grazed down to lower heights under continuous grazing, without depressing milk yield, as a result of the higher tiller density and denser swards when compared to rotationally grazed swards.

Figure 3.7 Effect of sward height on herbage intake under rotational grazing.

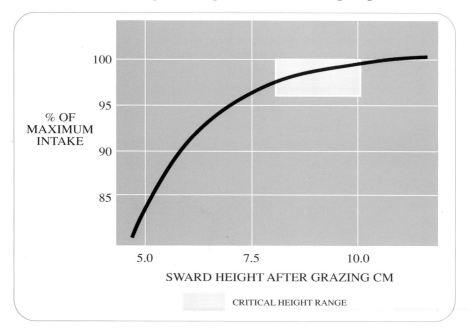

% OF MAXIMUM INTAKE

SWARD HEIGHT AFTER GRAZING CM

CRITICAL HEIGHT RANGE

Figure 3.8 Effect of sward height on herbage intake under continuous grazing.

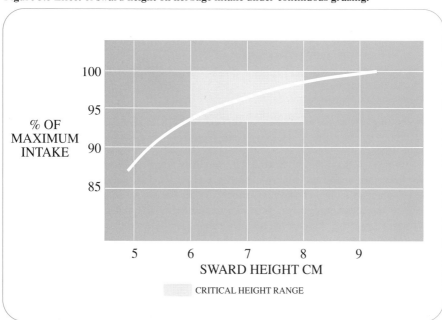

% OF MAXIMUM INTAKE

SWARD HEIGHT CM

CRITICAL HEIGHT RANGE

Typical stocking rates required to achieve these target heights for different site classes are given in Table 3.2.

Table 3.2   Stocking rates required to achieve target sward heights for different site classes (assuming optimum N levels applied)

	Sward height (cm)		Site Class 1	Site Class 2
	Rotational (after grazing)	Continuous (throughout grazing)	(cows/ha)	(cows/ha)
Time				
April-May	6-8	6	7	6
June-mid July	8	7	6	3
mid July - early Sept	8	8	5	2.5
Sept-housing	10	8-10	3	1.7

(b) Achieving target heights

In order to achieve the height targets recommended above, flexibility of management is essential.   This involves:

(i) *Using high stocking rates in the spring*

This minimises the heading and rejection of herbage and can be achieved by:

- turning out the cows on a tight stocking rate
- shutting up the maximum area for first cut silage

In many instances it is useful to nominally allocate part of the grazing area to first cut silage and manage accordingly. Should the need arise some of this area may be used for grazing before the silage cut is taken, whereas in good years an additional bonus area can be cut for silage. Similarly, further adjustments to the balance of silage/grazing areas can be made as the season progresses. It is also important to note that a 3 cut silage system allows more flexibility to alter the silage/grazing area balance than would be the case with a 2 cut system as discussed in Chapter 4.

(ii) *Using supplementary feeds*

By monitoring the sward height at regular intervals, imminent grass shortages can quickly be identified and buffer feeds introduced as required (see section 3.5).

3.4 CHOICE OF GRAZING SYSTEM

There are two major categories into which most grazing systems can be ascribed; rotational grazing and continuous grazing.

(a) Rotational grazing

This system provides, on a regular basis, fresh herbage that has not been cut or grazed for a period of at least 2 weeks.

(b) Continuous grazing

In this case pasture is grazed continuously through the season. In practice livestock may be removed for a short period of not more than 2 to 5 days at a time.

(c) Comparison of the systems

Most comparisons and surveys of the two systems have shown little or no difference in milk production, although there is evidence to indicate that rotational grazing systems may be more productive at higher stocking rates. For example, in a three-year study at Trawsgoed EHF, total lactation yields of spring calving cows on a rotational grazing system were 7% greater than those of cows continuously grazed at the same stocking rate.

In general, rotational grazing systems are easier to operate as they facilitate better assessment of the quantity and quality of herbage on offer. However, this must be balanced against the lower fencing costs and labour input required to operate a continuous grazing system which will generally also produce swards of higher tiller density.

(d) Factors influencing choice of system

(i) *Sward effects*
Rotational grazing can lead to severe but localised poaching in wet conditions, whereas more general but less severe soiling can occur with continuous grazing.

(ii) *Topography*
Farm layout can influence choice of system; for example, field size and presence of hilly areas. Provision of shelter from adverse weather is much easier with continuous grazing than in small paddocks.

(iii) *Herd requirements*
Cows with a high yield potential, for example spring calvers, may perform better under a rotational grazing system, reflecting the greater control of herbage availability.

(iv) *Management*
Rotational grazing permits much greater flexibility to undertake short-term changes in stocking density, for example by closing up or releasing paddocks for silage. This facilitates the attainment of sward height targets through the season. Under continuous

grazing surplus grass is not at a suitable stage for cutting for a further 3 weeks after it has been closed up.

(v) *Sward type*
Rotational grazing tends to favour the persistence of white clover in mixed grass/white clover swards. This system allows clover in the pasture to rejuvenate between grazings. However, continuous grazing systems on mixed swards have proved successful and the lower grass heights imposed may allow clover to spread more easily and attain a high proportion in the sward. Whichever system is preferred it is recommended that some periods of rest from grazing during the season are provided.

(e) Organisation of grazing systems

(i) *Rotational Grazing*
By using one day paddocks, it is possible to exert a high level of control over the supply of grass to the herd. As grass growth declines through the season, additional paddocks can be introduced to maintain grass supply giving a longer grazing cycle later in the season. By moving to a three day paddock system, fewer services are required but there is much greater fluctuation in the quantity and quality of grass available to the herd on a daily basis. A further refinement involves provision of three day paddocks with a flexible sub-fence for each feed. This approach combines the advantage of the one-day and three-day paddock systems in that grass availability and quality is easily monitored and the servicing requirements are reduced.

(ii) *Continuous grazing*
True continuous grazing involves using a single area which is grazed throughout the season, with the size of the area increased after each silage cut. However, dividing the area into day and night areas facilitates cow collection and enables a split-farm layout to be accommodated. Block grazing, a further refinement of continuous grazing involves subdividing the area into a number of convenient similarly-sized blocks, to which additional blocks are introduced as the season progresses. One grazing is taken from each block in sequence so introducing some of the flexibility associated with rotational grazing.

(f) Additional requirements

(i) *Water*
This must be available to the herd at all times. Grazing dairy cows can consume up to 100 litres of water per day and special attention should be paid to water supply in continuously . grazed fields as cows should not have to walk too far (more than 250 m) to water troughs. Water should also be made available in collecting yards and at the parlour exit.

(ii) *Mineral supplements*
Mineral deficiencies can occur in grazing cattle under certain conditions. For example, in areas where grass tetany (hypomagnesaemia) is a problem, additional magnesium (30 g per day) must be available, particularly in the spring and autumn. This can be given in the drinking water, in a small amount of a high magnesium concentrate, dusted on paddocks prior to grazing or by using a combination of approaches.

Other trace minerals such as copper, cobalt, manganese and iodine may be deficient in certain areas. In these circumstances the local advisory services should be consulted and trace element status checked by blood sampling a small proportion of animals in the herd before offering additional minerals.

3.5 ROLE OF CONCENTRATES AND OTHER SUPPLEMENTARY FEEDS

Since grazed grass is the cheapest feed available to the dairy cow, approximately one quarter the price of purchased concentrate, profitability depends on making full use of it before offering any additional feeds. However, in those herds where the aim is towards higher milk yields per cow, situations may arise where economic milk production responses may be obtained by provision of supplementary feeds, particularly in view of the higher prices for milk now being paid during the summer period. In the past concentrates have been used in this fashion, but latterly the concepts of 'partial storage feeding' and 'buffer feeding' have emerged, embracing a wider variety of additional forage or 'bulky' feeds. These various options are considered below.

(a) Concentrates

The feeding of concentrates will usually lead to some increase in yields of milk and milk solids. However, when grass is plentiful the feeding of extra energy as concentrates to grazing cows is generally uneconomic, since grass intake is depressed at such a rate that the increase in total intake is relatively small:

● **A little more milk may be produced but much of the additional energy is used for body weight gain.**

Recent studies have suggested that the extent of depression in herbage intake resulting from concentrate supplementation (substitution effect) is influenced by concentrate type. For example, high starch concentrates cause a greater depression in grass intake than high fibre concentrates. Consequently, larger (though still uneconomic) responses in milk yield have been obtained following supplementation with high fibre concentrates at pasture.

Nevertheless, the feeding of concentrates to grazing cows may be justified either if there is a shortage of grass or if the cow has a potential well above that suggested for grass in Figure 3.2, for example with June to August calvers. These situations are now considered in more detail.

(i) *Shortage of grass*
The feeding of concentrates may be justified when grass growth is slow or when sward heights fall below target, such that a marked depression in milk yield per cow is obtained. However, the amount that can be economically fed is still very limited. An example of this is shown in Figure 3.9.

Figure 3.9 The influence of herbage restriction for 2- and 5-week periods on milk production.

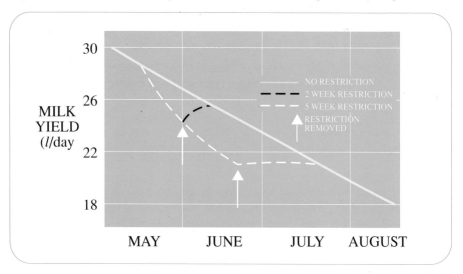

A severe shortage of grass for 2 weeks in late-May in a paddock grazing system (5 cm stubble height rather that the target 8 to 10 cm) reduced yield by 12%. Yield recovered quickly when adequate grass was again available. After a longer 5 weeks restriction the recovery was slower. However, the value of the milk lost over the period of restriction could only have bought 2 to 3 kg of concentrate per cow per day. Only when the shortage of grass is exceptionally severe should amounts of concentrate in excess of 2 to 3 kg/day be used, but it is unlikely that this level of supplementation would fully maintain yields. Concentrate feeding should be stopped once the target grazing heights are again achieved (Table 3.2). The height below which supplementary concentrates are justified may also vary for cows and herds of different milk yield levels.

(ii) *High yielding cows*
If the potential of the cow is substantially above the potential production from grass (Figure 3.2), then concentrate feeding may be economic. Substitution of grass by concentrate will occur and, as with silage-based diets, the extra output of milk solids may be disappointing. In these circumstances an increase in stocking rate must be made to utilise the forage released.

Little information is available to define the optimum level of concentrate but even with spring-calving cows yielding 35 kg/day at turnout an amount greater than 3 kg/day of conventional concentrate is unlikely to improve profitability. The situation is different with summer (June/July) calving cows, which have a high yield potential but must graze on swards declining in grass growth and quality from July to September. With this factor, along with the higher milk price currently paid at this time of year, concentrate levels of 5 to 6 kg/day can be justified for summer calving cows.

(b) Other supplementary feeds

Materials available as supplements to grass, other than concentrates, include straw, hay, brewers grains, distillers grains and forage crops, but grass silage is probably the most commonly used; perhaps in conjunction with one or more of the other feeds. The length of time that cows have access to the supplementary feed can vary from just a short period of about one hour after milking, a practice commonly called **'buffer feeding'**, to housing overnight, known as **'partial storage feeding'**. In both cases the objective is to overcome variations in grass supply to the grazing cow with bulky feed. Shortfalls in grass supply can arise deliberately, for example by the imposition of very high grazing stocking rates, in which case the supplementation forms part of the overall grazing strategy. Alternatively, it may be a consequence of short-term fluctuations in grass growth (eg, due to drought), a decline in grass quality or adverse weather conditions, when the supplement may be used tactically to overcome these more temporary shortages. Both buffer feeding and partial storage feeding can be used in the strategic or tactical senses.

Before embarking on a system incorporating the feeding of bulky supplements in addition to grazing it is important to define the objective of such an approach. A recent MMB survey of 98 'Milkminder' costed farms practising buffer feeding identified more than six reasons for its implementation, including:

- to improve UME output from grassland
- to improve milk quality
- to help overcome grass shortages in difficult weather conditions
- limitations of farm layout
- to increase margin over concentrates
- to increase stocking rate

Evidence to date suggests that the effects on both milk quality and UME output are variable and depend upon factors such as the quality and length of time of access to the supplement.

Supplementation with bulky feeds should be viewed principally as a means of ensuring a high degree of grass utilisation by giving the confidence to apply and maintain high grazing stocking rates. By so doing grazing quality will be maintained, with heading and herbage rejection minimised, without cow performance being penalised. The application of partial storage feeding and buffer feeding are considered in more detail below:

(i) *Partial storage feeding (day grazing with night housing)*

Early season

This technique is often effectively practised in early season as a means of supporting very high grazing stocking rates, in particular for autumn-calving cows, so allowing a large acreage to be closed up for first-cut silage. It has the added advantage of avoiding inclement night weather. Cows should be given *ad libitum* access to the overnight feed and it should be of good quality (silage 65+ D-value), otherwise yields of milk and milk solids will be reduced. The reduction in butterfat content of milk at turnout can be effectively countered by partial storage feeding, but this may be offset by a fall in protein percentage. If silage of only moderate quality is available it is better mixed with more palatable materials such as brewers or distillers grains. Even in these circumstances partial storage feeding is unlikely to improve performance over conventional grazing and it should be used in early season solely as an aid to grassland management. Grazing stocking rates should be about 10-11 cows/ha.

Mid to late season

As the grazing season progresses, grass growth rate declines and herbage quality and palatability diminish due to increased rejection, particularly under lax management. Under these circumstances feeding silage overnight may improve total nutrient intake, possibly leading to improved output of milk solids and certainly increasing liveweight gain.

At this time silage may be eaten in preference to grass and intakes of silage will be higher than in early season. To ensure a high level of grass utilisation is maintained, the reduction in grass intake must be countered by a tight grazing policy during the day (6-7 cows/ha).

(ii) *Buffer feeding (post-milking access to supplement)*

Buffer feeding is the simplest means of offering supplementary feeds whilst still realising the full potential of grazed grass. Cows are allowed access to the buffer for a period of about one hour after one or both milkings. Intakes of the buffer feed increase gradually through the grazing season but can fluctuate day-to-day according to climatic conditions (Figure 3.10). However, because the buffer contributes less to the total nutrient intake than in partial storage feeding, its impact on cow performance is less marked. Thus, yields of milk and milk solids and liveweight gain are generally similar between conventionally grazed and buffer fed cows throughout the grazing season. The buffer fed cows should be about 20% more tightly stocked than cows which are only grazed according to the stocking rate and sward height guidelines given in Table 3.2. However, the period of access to buffer feed should be regulated to ensure that grass wastage does not occur on the grazed area, as a consequence of cows preferring to consume the buffer. Using this approach may facilitate a carryover of extra silage for winter feeding. On the other hand, too free access to the buffer will result in poorer grass utilisation and a shortfall in winter forage stocks to the detriment of feed costs.

Figure 3.10 Intake of buffer fed silage through the grazing season.

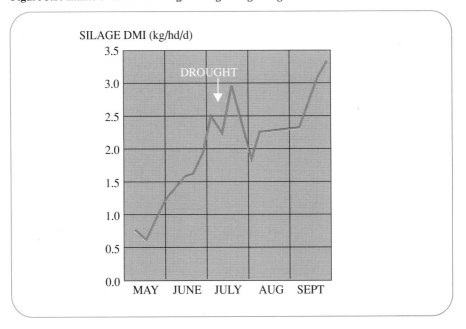

(iii) *Establishing a buffer feeding system*

The farmer is not immediately in a position to supplement grazed grass with silage as a bulky feed unless silage is left over from the winter. This applies particularly to those intending to use partial storage feeding with its higher bulky feed requirement. Establishing a home grown supplement supply for this purpose entails following the grazing guidelines above but perhaps supporting these with purchased bulky feed for early season. Alternatively, cows could continue to be housed and zero grazing used to maintain very high grazing stocking rates until the first cut of silage. In the case of buffer feeding the requirement for supplement in early season is very much less (Figure 3.10) than for partial storage feeding. Provided high grazing stocking rates are applied at this time (7-8 cows/ha), it may be possible to commence buffer feeding newly made silage soon after first cut. Beyond this time no opportunity should be lost to ensile surplus grass, particularly in the autumn.

Another alternative is to make some big bale silage in the season prior to that in which buffer feeding is to commence. This can then be used to initially implement the system. The higher stocking rates will then allow more clamp silage to be made to provide a bulky feed for the next season. However, it should always be remembered that all bulky feeds need to be of high feeding quality and offered *ad libitum,* and cows must have access to water during buffer feeding.

(c) Buffer grazing

An alternative approach to using silage or other bulky feeds as a buffer to grazing is the buffer grazing approach. This approach can be used with continuous grazing to enable better utilization of grass and response to variable grass growth in early season. The technique involves the use of an electric fence to create a "buffer" of herbage along one side of the grazed area. If grass growth is particularly good in early season, this buffer may be surplus to requirements and can be conserved as silage. In other situations, where grass growth is poor in early season, a large part of the buffer can be grazed off. An essential part of this approach is the use of sward height measurements to assess the level of grass utilization on the main grazing area.

3.6 CONCLUSIONS

Grazed grass is the cheapest available feed for dairy cows and profitable milk production relies on efficient grazing systems which enable good utilization of the grass crop. In many instances the full potential of grazed grass is not achieved at farm level largely as a result of insufficient confidence in grass. This lack of confidence may result from variations in grass growth both within and between years and from problems in efficiently utilizing grass, particularly on heavy soils in wet years. However, recent developments in the understanding of grass growth and in the concept of sward height measurement provides a stimulus to milk producers to reassess their grazing management strategies.

The key features of an efficient grazing management strategy are as follows:

- From a knowledge of grass growing conditions (site class) and fertilizer use (Chapter 1) calculate an appropriate long term target stocking rate.

- Areas need to be clearly allocated for grazing through the season. This will depend on silage making policy (one, two or multicut system).

  Note. More frequent silage cutting systems increase the flexibility to introduce or remove areas from the grazing system.

- Monitor grazing sward heights through the season, using 'average grass height' with continuous grazing or 'average height of stubble remaining after grazing' with rotational grazing.

- If grass heights increase above target, reduce the grazing area by taking an area out for silage making.

- If grass heights fall below target, increase the grazing area by introducing silage aftermaths. If aftermaths not available then consider use of silage as a buffer feed or in extreme situations introduce concentrate supplementation.

- In areas prone to summer drought conditions consider use of forage crops, buffer feeding or partial storage feeding although it is important to note that, per unit of energy, silage is three to four times the cost of grazed grass.

- With high-yielding spring calving cows, buffer feeding of silage during August, September and October can produce worthwhile responses in milk yield coinciding with a high milk price.

- With summer calving dairy herds, where the principal aim is to produce milk in the high priced period from July to October, grazing management in early season should be targeted towards achieving low sward heights (below 6 cm) during April and May.

This will encourage better performance from grass in mid and late season.

CHAPTER 4

THE INTEGRATION OF CONSERVATION WITH GRAZING

George Fisher and Sinclair Mayne

4.1 Principles of Integration
4.2 Achieving the Integration of Conservation with Grazing
4.3 Factors Influencing the Grazing/Conservation System
4.4 Achieving the Correct Balance of Grazing and Conservation
4.5 Conclusions

4.1 PRINCIPLES OF INTEGRATION

The aims of grassland management during the summer period are twofold: firstly to produce sufficient high quality silage for winter feeding and secondly to maintain a high efficiency of grazing. To achieve this an effective system integrating silage making and grazing must be employed, thereby achieving maximum use of the available grassland with minimum wastage. Integration is difficult and the implementation of any system employed on individual farms will be influenced by many factors including:

- general grass growing conditions (site class)
- variation in grass growing conditions within and between growing seasons
- herd size and calving pattern
- quantity and quality of silage required

The seasonal pattern of grass production (see Figure 1.4) is characterised by a peak in grass growth in May-June followed by a decline in mid and late season. In order to utilise grass efficiently, the removal of grass through a combination of cutting for silage and consumption by the grazing animal must match the pattern of grass production. Integration of cutting and grazing management is therefore crucial to efficient milk production and any system requires:

- careful planning before each grass growing season
- flexibility to react to above or below average grass production and weather conditions.

(a) Matching Grass Growth to the Requirements of the Herd

The cow requires an adequate supply of high quality, fresh grass throughout the grazing season. Therefore, the amount of grass available must be matched with the requirements of the herd. A comparison of the seasonal availability of grass, in terms of Metabolisable Energy (ME), with the requirements of spring calving cows over the grazing season shows the major problem in grassland management (Figure 4.1).

Figure 4.1 The ME requirements of spring calving cows at three stocking rates compared with the seasonal production of metabolisable energy from grass under grazing.

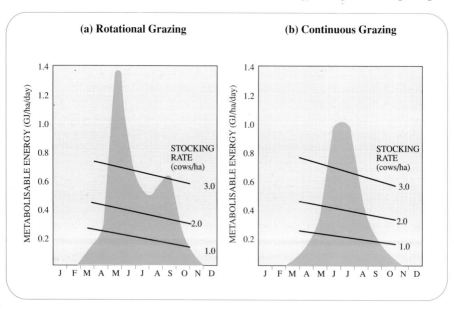

If a constant stocking rate is maintained throughout the season, then the rapid growth of grass early in the season leads to an excess. Raising the stocking rate to overcome this creates a deficit in late season. Therefore, in order to meet the requirements of the cow and maintain the efficiency of grazing, the stocking rate must be changed over the season.

The principal means of varying the stocking rate is to close up areas of land and to conserve the grass for winter feed.

Adjustments can also be made by:

- supplementation during periods of grass shortage
- changing the pattern of grass growth through alternative patterns of nitrogen fertilizer application.
- introducing additional livestock during periods of excess grass

These secondary measures are strategic in nature and can be used to provide flexibility within and between grass growing seasons.

74

The conservation of grass, therefore, is not only a means of providing winter feed, but is also a way of controlling grass surpluses and thereby making more efficient use of grazed grass. During the winter, a relatively uniform conserved forage can be fed as required and this contrasts with the grazing period when pasture must be grazed within strict time periods if quality is to be maintained. Therefore, the first step to effective integration must be to consider the quantity and quality of grass required for grazing and for silage.

(b) Timing of Operations

Silage quantity and quality is largely determined by the timing and frequency of cutting. As the yield of any cut is allowed to bulk up, the feed value of the grass falls. However, the net effect is a greater total yield of feed energy. Thus, less frequent cutting has been thought to result in more milk being produced per hectare, provided that the chosen cutting strategy has no effect on the grazing of silage aftermaths. However, in practice the time at which grass regrowth, after cutting, is available for grazing is very important if both the quantity and quality of grazed grass is to be maintained. Consequently, less frequent cutting will not always result in higher milk production per hectare.

4.2 ACHIEVING THE INTEGRATION OF CONSERVATION WITH GRAZING

(a) Aims of a Grazing/Silage System

The principal aim of the overall grazing/silage system is to grow and utilise the maximum amount of home grown forage. This implies producing high levels of herbage by using the target nitrogen levels given in Chapter 1. However, there is no point in producing large quantities of grass if it is not converted into animal product. Thus, setting and achieving high standards of efficiency is important to the system.

(b) Measurement of Efficiency

Since losses in silage making are likely to be independent of cutting frequency, the overall efficiency of grassland management can be measured by the proportion of grass available for grazing that is eaten by the herd. This is termed **'grazing efficiency.'** At one extreme, when grazing efficiency is in excess of 100 %, it means that grass is not available to meet all the requirements of the cow. At the other extreme, low values mean that grass is being wasted.

The aim should be to achieve a grazing efficiency of 80 % over the whole season. Higher values than this (up to 100 %) can be sustained for short periods of about 2 weeks, but longer periods at higher efficiencies will result in a reduction in grass intake and milk yield.

The output of the combined conservation and grazing system is measured by the total amount of energy produced from grass that is consumed by the cow. This is termed the

Utilised Metabolisable Energy (UME) from grass and it is expressed as Gigajoules (GJ) of Metabolisable Energy (ME) per hectare (1 GJ = 1000 MJ). Since grass yield and hence energy are lower under poorer grass growing conditions, the target UME falls from site class 1 to 5 (see Chapter 1 for definitions of site classes). Nevertheless, within any one site class the aim should be to achieve target UME values. The achieved UME values for a particular farm can be readily calculated by the local nutritional adviser and these should be compared with the values in Table 4.1 as a guide to the present level of efficiency.

Table 4.1 Target Utilised Metabolisable Energy (UME) values at different site classes.

Site class	Target UME (GJ/ha)
1	126
2	115
3	105
4	93
5	83

Many different analyses have shown that conservation/grazing strategies which produce the highest UME values usually result in the highest gross margin per hectare and per litre. In order to achieve the target UME levels shown in Table 4.1, wastage of grass must be kept to a minimum. This involves:

● Use of high grazing stocking rates in early season when grass growth is at a peak (see Chapter 3)

● Phasing of silage cuts to ensure optimum production of first cut material and availability of silage aftermaths in late season when grass growth declines.

(c) Factors Affecting the Choice of System

At the outset, it is important to ensure that the overall stocking rate on the farm takes account of:

● Grass growing conditions (site class)
● Target milk yield per cow
● Level of concentrate usage

Once the overall target stocking rate has been decided, the priorities of the system in terms of grazing or conservation need to be determined. For example, in the case of late winter or spring calving cows, good grazing management will have greater impact on overall performance than would be the case with autumn calving cows. In contrast, the quantity and quality of forage conserved will have a much greater impact on autumn calving herds. For summer calving cows, grazing and conservation management will both have large affects on efficiency and profitability.

(d) Planning a Grazing/Silage System

Having established the overall requirements of the grazing/silage system, detailed planning can then be undertaken. Systems should be matched to the calving pattern and, thereby, the nutritional requirements of the herd. The simplest situations to manage in terms of integrating grazing and cutting are those based on block calved herds. In these cases, the requirements of the whole herd are distinct and the system can be managed accordingly. For example, with a spring calving herd more emphasis can be placed on the grazing areas to optimise production from spring grass, while for an autumn calving herd the emphasis can be placed on making high quality silage to achieve good production during the winter. The integration of grazing and cutting is more difficult with herds comprising groups of cows which block calve at different times of the year. The most difficult systems to manage are those based on all year round calving and where the cows are not block calved. The majority of dairy farms in the U.K. have an all year round calving policy and with this type of herd structure, the grazing/cutting system must be balanced to provide high quality forage throughout the year as grazing or silage. Examples of strategies are outlined below:

(i) *Spring Calving System*

Target grazing stocking rates are shown in Table 4.2 for spring calving cows with overall targets of:

- Lactation yield 5500 litres
- Concentrate usage 0.5 t/cow
- Silage requirement 10 t/cow

With spring calving cows, a good supply of grass throughout the grazing season is essential, whilst minimising wastage in early season. Consequently, consideration should be given to the use of buffer feeding in mid and late season, particularly if sward heights fall below the target values given in Chapter 3, Table 3.2.

Table 4.2 Target grazing stocking rates through the grazing season for spring calving cows (assuming target N levels applied)

Time	Site class				
	1	2	3	4	5
April - May	7	6	6	5	5
June - mid July	6	3	2.5	2	1.75
Mid July - early September	5	2.5	2	1.5	1
September - housing	3	1.75	1.5	1.25	1

Note: Buffer feeding may be required, particularly in site classes 3–5.

(ii) *Autumn Calving System*

Target stocking rates are also given in Table 4.3 for autumn calving cows with overall targets of:

- Lactation yield 5500 litres
- Concentrate usage 1.0 t/cow
- Silage requirement 10 t/cow

In the case of autumn calving cows nearing the end of lactation at the start of the grazing season, the supply of grass is less critical, with the aim being to maximise both the quality and quantity of herbage for conservation. For this reason, much higher grazing stocking rates can be used, enabling a high efficiency of utilisation of grass during the grazing period.

Table 4.3 **Target grazing stocking rates through the grazing season for autumn calving cows (assuming target N levels applied)**

Time	Site class				
	1	2	3	4	5
April - May	8	7	7	7	7
June - mid July	7	7	6	5	4
Mid July - early September	7	6	4	3	2
September - housing	3	3	3	2	2

In herds where there is a move towards late autumn calving, it may be possible to increase the stocking rates in early season above those given in Table 4.3, but some reduction in stocking rate would be required following calving.

The target grazing stocking rates given in Tables 4.2 and 4.3 provide useful guidelines for long term planning purposes. However, as a result of year to year variations in the pattern of grass growth, measurements of sward height should be taken on a regular basis to enable short term adjustments of the grazing stocking rate.

(iii) *Areas for Grazing/Conservation*

Once the target stocking rate, yield and concentrate use have been established, it is possible to decide on which areas of the farm should be reserved for grazing or cutting at different stages of the growing season. On individual farms this will be influenced by:

- calving pattern (silage requirement)
- desired digestibility of silage
- grass growing conditions
- topography/soil type

Examples of target areas for cutting and grazing are shown in Table 4.4. The figures are based on three silage cuts and target rates of nitrogen fertilizer applications on a site class 1 or 2 farm.

Table 4.4   Areas required (ha) for silage and grazing (100 cow herd, overall stocking rate 2.5 cows/ha)

	Autumn calvers			Spring calvers		
	Graze	Cut	% area cut	Graze	Cut	% area cut
First cut	14	26	**65**	20	20	**50**
Second cut	24	16	**40**	24	16	**40**
Third cut	28	12	**30**	28	12	**30**
Aftermaths	40	0	**0**	40	0	**0**

The grazing area should **not be more** and the silage area should **not be less** than that shown in Table 4.4 under normal conditions.

(iv) *Summer Calving Cows*

Following increased payments from the UK Milk Marketing Boards for milk produced in mid and late summer, the number of cows calving in the May to July period has increased. The peak yield and intake requirement of these cows coincides with declining grass growth and quality. This complicates the integration of grazing and cutting on farms where a proportion of the herd are summer calvers and the rest are spring or autumn calving.

Few herds will contain only summer calvers, but where this is the case there must be emphasis on providing high quality grazing in mid and late season and cutting the maximum area of high quality first cut silage for winter feeding.

The more usual situation is where only a proportion of the herd are summer calving. In this case management is aided if these cows can be treated as a separate group. The summer calvers can then be integrated into the cutting/grazing system by being tightly stocked during the dry period and provided with the best grazing in mid season at a stocking rate of about 4.5 cows/ha.

On many farms it will not be possible to treat the summer calvers as a separate group and following calving they will have to graze with the rest of the herd. In this situation the integration of the summer calvers into the cutting/grazing system can be most difficult. To overcome the potential problems there is a tendency to provide high concentrate inputs for the summer calvers and forage buffers for the whole herd. However, profit margins will be maximised if concentrate supplementation and buffer feeding are kept to a minimum. This can be achieved by applying high stocking rates in spring, which will produce good quality swards for summer calvers in mid and late season, and by making sure that the maximum area is cut for high quality silage. The provision of forage buffers may still be necessary, however, particularly where grass growth is reduced by weather conditions and/or there is a lack of grazing available for freshly calved cows between first cut silage and the regrowths becoming available for use.

4.3 FACTORS INFLUENCING THE GRAZING/CONSERVATION SYSTEM

Factors which influence the efficiency of grassland management and the choice of the most appropriate system of integration are:

- quality of grass cut for silage (number of cuts)
- timing of cuts
- grass growing conditions

In the discussion which follows it is assumed that the target milk yield is 6000 l and the silage requirements are those set out in Figure 2.7 and target levels of fertilizer nitrogen appropriate to site class (Chapter 1) are used.

(a) Quality of Grass Cut for Silage (number of cuts)

The quality of silage required for feeding cows during the winter determines the number of cuts taken. Systems which rely on a single, heavy cut to meet silage requirements in terms of quantity result in low quality forage (61 D, 10.1 ME). More frequent cutting is required to produce silage of a high quality (67 D, 11.1 ME).

Less grass is wasted in two- and three-cut systems and grazing efficiency approaches the target of 80%. The potential of single cut systems to produce large quantities of grass for conservation in early and mid season is more than offset by the inefficient use of grass on grazed areas.

The wastage of grass under grazing occurs mainly in May, July, August and early September. The fact that greater wastage occurs in one-cut systems rather than two- and three-cut systems is the result of a combination of various factors:

- a fixed area of land is closed up for conservation for a longer period making it difficult to balance grazing and conservation needs in early season.
- a heavier crop is cut later and regrowth is therefore slower.
- the land available for grazing is severely restricted in mid season until regrowth is available.
- a larger area of land is released into the grazing cycle in a period when the requirements of the cow are relatively low in relation to grass growth.

Frequent cutting results in greater flexibility and in more effective management of grass for grazing. Improved efficiency of utilisation of grazed grass in one-cut systems can be achieved by reducing fertilizer inputs later in the season. This inevitably means lower UME outputs due to the reduced amount of grass grown.

(b) Timing of Cuts

Within any cutting system there is some flexibility in the times at which the cuts are taken for conservation. If silage of very high quality (68 D+) is required then three cuts need to be taken at 4 to 5 week intervals. However, the regrowth period after the first cut can be extended to 6 weeks in a three-cut system (mid May, end June, mid August) or 8 weeks in a two-cut system (end May, end July). This extension of the regrowth period has only a small effect on average quality since the first cut represents the biggest proportion of the total silage yield.

Extending the regrowth period in this manner has a marked effect on grazing management. By moving from a 4- to 6-week regrowth in a three-cut system, the second and third cuts are taken later in the year and this results in less wastage of grass for grazing in mid and late season. A similar effect occurs in moving from a 6- to 8-week regrowth in a two-cut system.

Late summer and autumn cuts

Consideration should be given to taking cuts of grass for silage in the late summer or autumn since considerable wastage of grass can occur in this period. This is particularly important with cutting strategies designed to produce silage either of very high (68 D+) or low (61 D) quality where the last cut would otherwise be completed by mid season. The effect in both these systems is to improve grazing efficiency and UME output by taking a late summer/autumn cut.

With other cutting strategies an autumn cut for silage can be useful to meet changes in the year to year variability in grass growth.

Autumn grass tends to be wetter and contain less sugars than spring or summer grass. When ensiled, its value for milk production may be slightly less or similar to that of spring grass with equal digestibility, provided it is well preserved by using the levels of silage additive suggested in Chapter 2.

Table 4.5   Alternative silage making strategies.

Aim		Strategy
Silage of very high quality (68 D+, ME 11.2+)	4 cuts —	mid May, mid June mid July, mid August
Silage of high quality (67 D, ME 11.1)	3 cuts —	mid May, end June mid August
Silage of medium quality (64 D, ME 10.6)	2 cuts —	end May, end July
Silage of low quality (61 D, ME 10.1)	2 cuts —	mid June, end August
Silage of very low quality (57 D, ME 9.4)	1 cut —	late June

The superiority of two-, three- and four-cut systems over the one-cut strategy in providing a better balance of grazing and conservation needs is seen over all sites. However, the relative ranking in the above systems in terms of grazing efficiency and UME output depends on grass growing conditions (site class).

(c) Grass Growing Conditions

A comparison of the strategies at different site classes is shown in Figure 4.2. In good grass growing conditions there is little difference in grazing efficiency and UME output between two-, three- and four-cut systems. A great deal of flexibility therefore exists in the choice of silage quality and hence cutting strategy. However, as grass growing conditions become poorer the strategies of producing medium to high quality silage give the highest grazing efficiencies and UME outputs.

There is a more rapid change in grass growth between early and mid season at the poorer sites (site classes 4 and 5) and thus the early cutting, associated with medium and high quality silage systems, is essential in order to release land and provide sufficient grass for grazing in mid and late June.

The two cut strategy to produce silage of low quality in poor grass growing conditions suffers the same disadvantage as the one-cut system, in that land for grazing is severely limited following cutting. Further, the cutting of heavy crops at infrequent intervals (i.e. mid June and late August) is likely to lead to a rapid deterioration of the sward. In dry areas early cutting is essential to ensure recovery of aftermaths and adequate growth in mid season.

Separate conservation and grazing areas.

On most farms the area of land required for grazing will need to be increased as the grazing season progresses. Ideally, all fields that are cut for silage in early and mid season should be capable of subsequently being grazed by the herd. However, the layout of the farm may make this difficult or impossible. In such situations the correct balance between cutting and grazing can only be achieved by:

- utilising late summer and autumn growth on the cutting area, e.g. by late cuts of silage, zero grazing or by grazing with other livestock

- using supplementary feed (forage or concentrate) to reduce the grazing requirements at critical times in the season

- adjusting grass growth with nitrogen, e.g. applying more to the grazed area in mid season and less to the conservation block in late season.

Some of these options are inconvenient and may reduce overall grass production and it is obviously desirable to attempt to integrate some of the cutting and grazing areas. The following should be noted:

Figure 4.2 Effect of cutting strategy on grazing efficiency and UME output at different sites.

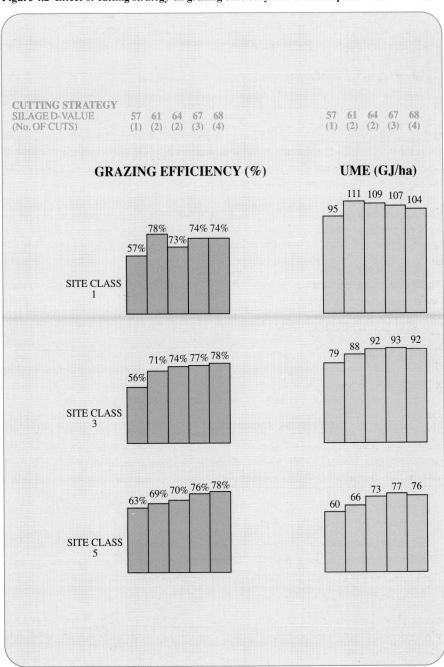

- constant cutting, especially at infrequent intervals, reduces tillering and makes the sward more open, which leads to a reduction in yield and an increase in the prevalence of weed species.

- grazing can restore sward structure and improve persistency and yield by encouraging new tiller growth

- if the cut swards in the conservation block can not be grazed then the use of specialist early leys, based on Italian ryegrass or hybrids, which can have high yields in their first year, should be considered.

4.4 ACHIEVING THE CORRECT BALANCE OF GRAZING AND CONSERVATION

The sections above have dealt with the principles and practice of management systems which integrate cutting and grazing activities on grassland dairy farms. The largest single factor which influences the success of these systems is grass growth and thus weather conditions. While the variability of grass growing conditions within and between seasons at any one site is outwith management control, there are various strategies which can be employed to negate these variations. These strategic management tools include:

- use of forage buffers
- use of concentrates
- use of nitrogen fertilizer.

The use of forage buffers and concentrates for grazing cows has been discussed in Chapter 3 and the use of additional N to increase yield of grass was considered in Chapter 1. These strategies alone or in combination will not make for the success of a cutting/ grazing system. However, their use can help to even out the detrimental effects of variable grass growth within and between seasons and aid the efficient use of grass. The desired balance between cutting and grazing for the chosen system can thus be maintained.

(a) Use of Forage Buffers and Concentrates

The danger of placing too much emphasis on making large amounts of high quality silage is that too great an area can be locked up for conservation, creating short-term shortages of grass for grazing. This occurs particularly in periods of drought when extra pressure is placed on silage and grazing areas, and where regrowth of silage aftermaths is delayed. In this situation, where grass heights fall below target (Table 3.2), forage buffers or concentrates may be used to supplement cow intake.

Supplementary feeding of grazing dairy cows is a common practice. As discussed in Chapter 3, responses to supplementary concentrates are generally uneconomic. Even in periods of extreme drought and shortage of grass, economic responses in milk yield to feeding proprietary concentrates will only be achieved if the level fed does not exceed 2 to 3 Kg per cow per day.

One solution may be to use silage rather than concentrates as the supplementary feed, by forage buffer or storage feeding. Even so with the real costs of silage in excess of £80/t DM, the milk response still needs to be in excess of 0.4Kg per Kg DM of silage to be economic.

The ideal supplement to the grazing dairy cow must clearly be other grazed grass. It is the cheapest feed available and there is no problem of feed substitution. This is the strength of the buffer grazing system which involves keeping a proportion of the grazing area to be cut or grazed as necessary.

(b) Use of N

Additional applications of N can be used to increase grass growth and thereby alleviate shortages of grass for grazing or cutting. This strategy can be employed provided that application rates do not exceed the recommended values and application practice is not outwith the codes identified in Chapter 1. However, the additional grass produced must be utilised efficiently if this strategy is to be economic and in drought situations, the higher applications of N will not produce more grass in the period of shortage. If extra grass produced is not utilised, then a financial loss will be incurred.

Alternatively, the total level of N applied may be held constant, but the amount applied at various times during the season altered to adjust the pattern of grass growth. The effect of changes in N application pattern on the seasonality of grass growth is illustrated in Figure 4.3. The ability to adjust growth is limited, but the technique is useful in situations where increased grass requirements coincide with the normal reduction in grass growth rate and quality. For example, on areas reserved for grazing summer calving cows, the shifting of the largest applications of N from April and May to June and July will favour grass growth in mid and late season when the summer calvers have their peak intake requirement.

Figure 4.3   The effect of pattern of fertilizer nitrogen application on pattern of grass growth and annual yield of grass, receiving 300 kg N/ha, at site class 3.

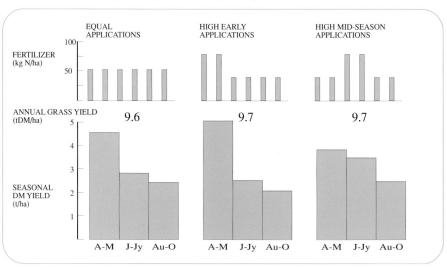

Adapted from IGER Technical Report No. 27 "The response of perennial ryegrass to fertilizer nitrogen in relation to climate and soil" – J. Morrison, M. V. Jackson and P. E. Sparrow.

4.5 CONCLUSIONS

● The role of forage conservation is not only to produce fodder for the dairy cow during the winter, but also to aid the management of grass for grazing. The strategy for conservation in terms of the timing and number of cuts influences the yield and quality of grass for silage and also the grass available for grazing over the season.

● Strategies involving two, three or four cuts result in higher outputs of UME and greater profitability than one-cut systems as a result of a more efficient use of grass for grazing.

● In good grass growing conditions there is considerable flexibility in the choice of silage quality provided that more than one cut is taken. However, as grass growing conditions become poorer strategies to produce silage of medium to high quality result in the highest UME outputs and profits. In these conditions the objectives should be to take an early first cut followed by one or two cuts at 8 or 6 week intervals, respectively.

● Late summer and autumn cuts, or preferably autumn grazing, are essential elements of the strategy if the objective is to achieve silage of either very high or low quality since the last cut in both of these systems would otherwise be taken too early.

● Separate conservation and grazing areas will lead to less efficient use of grass. Where possible fields used for conservation should be grazed in late season.

● Flexibility is vital to grassland management. The flexibility associated with frequent cutting to produce silage of medium to high quality is essential to take account of variation in grass growth both within and between seasons. Once an integrated cutting/grazing system has been chosen and planned, the additional strategies of buffer feeding, buffer grazing and manipulation of N fertilizer applications can aid in maintaining the correct balance in periods of grass shortage or excess. This is illustrated in the decision charts shown in Figures 4.4 and 4.5.

Figure 4.4 Decision chart for below average grass growth.

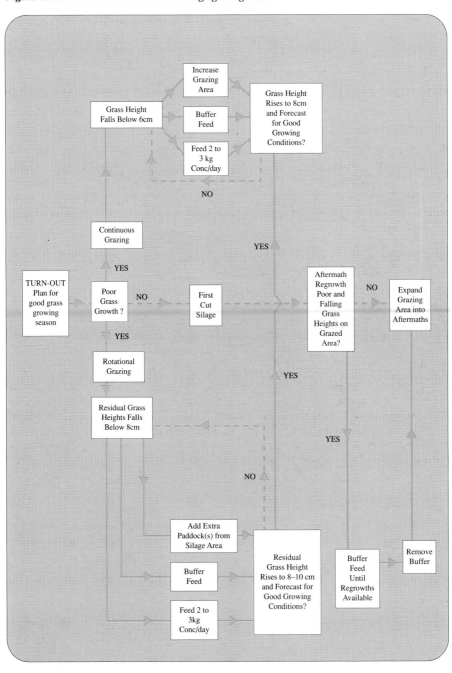

Figure 4.5 Decision chart for above average grass growth.

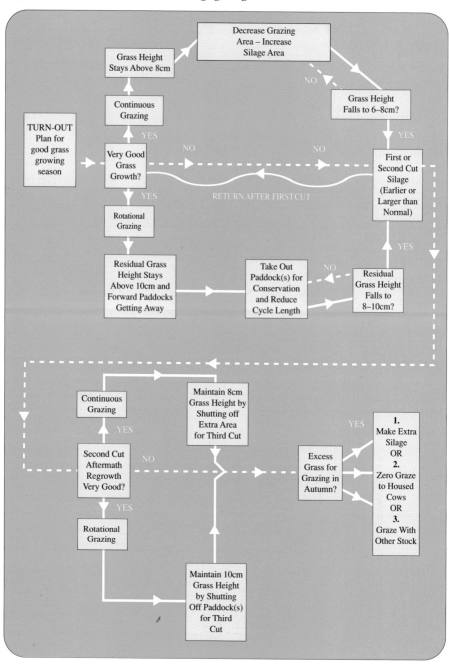

CHAPTER 5

ECONOMICS OF PRODUCTION
Chris Doyle and Stuart Goldie

5.1 Costs of milk production
5.2 Making better use of grass is the secret of success
5.3 Potential for profitable milk production from grass
5.4 Increasing profits from grass - a case study
5.5 Profit from grass - conclusion

Well managed grassland is the key to financial success in dairy farming. This is no more true than at present, when the Quota regime means that milk output from the herd cannot be increased, except by buying additional quota. In these circumstances, the emphasis must be on containing costs. As the cheapest feed for dairy cows, grass must play a major role in any drive to lower production costs and boost profits.

This chapter shows how making better use of grass can markedly improve profits. The potential for profitable milk production from grass is outlined and ways of increasing profits through better grassland management are discussed. Various measures of financial efficiency are used and these are summarised in Appendix 5.1.

5.1 COST OF MILK PRODUCTION

A typical breakdown of the costs and returns from producing a litre of milk for herds recorded in 1989-90 is shown in Figure 5.1.

Figure 5.1 Typical breakdown of the costs and returns per litre of milk for herds recorded in 1989-90

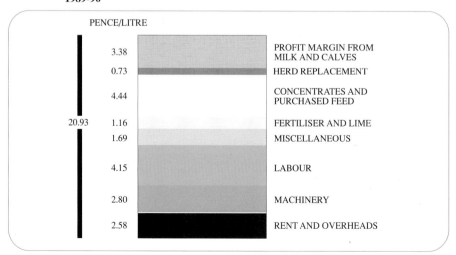

PENCE/LITRE		
	3.38	PROFIT MARGIN FROM MILK AND CALVES
	0.73	HERD REPLACEMENT
	4.44	CONCENTRATES AND PURCHASED FEED
20.93	1.16	FERTILISER AND LIME
	1.69	MISCELLANEOUS
	4.15	LABOUR
	2.80	MACHINERY
	2.58	RENT AND OVERHEADS

Sales of milk and calves brought in 20.93 pence per litre, of which 17.55 pence were swallowed up by costs. The main cost items were clearly feed, labour and rent/overheads. If expenditure of fertilizer to produce forage is included, then the costs of home-grown and purchased feed accounted for 5.6 pence or 27% of the total income from milk.

With strict limits on milk output under the Quota system, the key indicator of profitability is the **margin per litre**. Except where extra quota can be purchased, profits from the dairy herd can only be increased by reducing the costs of milk production. This means not only lowering feed costs per litre, but also containing fixed costs such as labour, machinery and overheads.

The importance of keeping a tight control over expenditure on feed is evident if the **margin over feed and forage (MOFF)** for the top and bottom 25% of dairy herds, ranked by margin per litre in the ICI DAIRYMAID scheme for 1988-89, is compared with the average. This comparison is shown in Figure 5.2.

Figure 5.2 Comparison of the top and bottom 25% of milk producers, ranked by margin per litre, in the ICI DAIRYMAID scheme in 1988-89.

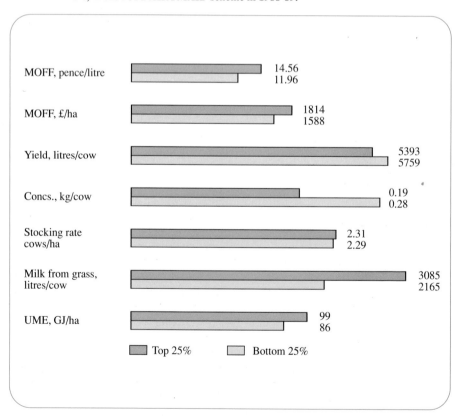

Looking at the results for the top 25% of herds, it can be seen that they obtained a much larger proportion of their milk from grass, while still maintaining milk yields. So their milk output from forage was 40% higher and the utilised metabolisable energy from grass (UME) was 15% higher than the average. The result was that MOFF was 2.6 pence/litre higher for the top herds, representing a profit margin of £13,000 for a typical herd, with a milk quota of 500,000 litres.

5.2 MAKING BETTER USE OF GRASS IS THE SECRET OF SUCCESS

On average in 1988-89, forage accounted for only 23% of feed costs, but supplied 72% of the energy needs of the cows (Figure 5.3) and among the top herds, the factors which contributed most to high margins per litre were:

● quantity of silage made
● quality of silage.

The top herds were making in excess of **10 tonnes of silage per cow with an average D-value in excess of 66.**

Figure 5.3   Relative contributions of forage to feed costs and energy requirements for the average DAIRYMAID HERD in 1988-89.

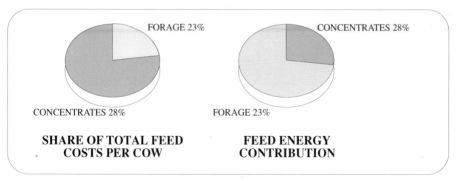

(a) Grass and Silage as Cheap Feeds

That grazed grass and silage represent cheap feeds can be seen if their costs of production are compared with their value as feedingstuffs. The average costs of producing and, where necessary, harvesting and ensiling grass are shown in Figure 5.4. Also shown are the values of grazed grass and average (62D) and good-quality (68D) silage as feeds for dairy cows, relative to barley costing £100/tonne and soya bean meal costing £170/tonne. Thus, good-quality grass silage cost £67/tonne to make, but was worth £116/tonne as a feed. By comparison, grazed grass cost around £39/tonne to produce, but was worth about £120/tonne as a feed. For comparison, the comparable costs and feed values for maize gluten, distillers grains and molassed beet pulp are also shown. For these latter feeds, costs have been equated with the **price at which they can be bought** on the open market.

Figure 5.4 Average costs of grazed grass, average and good-quality silage, maize gluten, distillers grains and molassed beet pulp, together with their values as feeds relative to barley at £100/tonne and soya bean meal at £170/tonne.

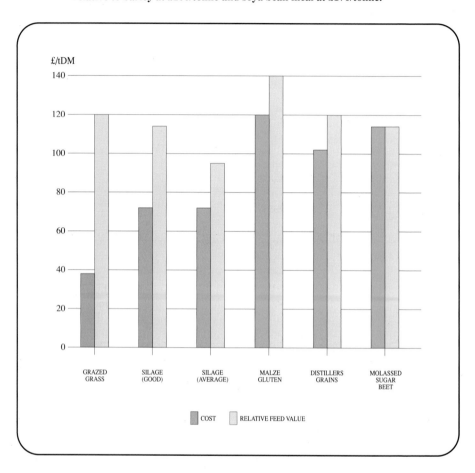

(b) Grassland Management and Profitability

How good grassland management can influence overall profitability is well illustrated by the comparative **MOFF** for two groups of herds within the DAIRYMAID scheme for 1987-88. The first group comprised a number of winter-calving herds, which were distinguished by their high reliance on forage - the **HIGH FORAGE** group. The second group consisted of a number of well-managed spring calving herds, which apparently made extremely efficient use of grazed grass - the **SPRING CALVING** group. The physical and financial performance of the two groups have been compared in Figure 5.5 with the averages for all herds in the DAIRYMAID scheme in that year.

Figure 5.5 Physical and financial performance of two groups of herds relative to the DAIRYMAID average for 1987-88.

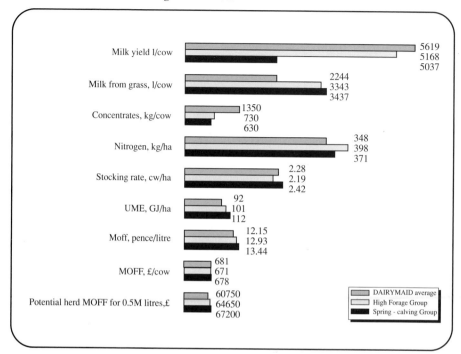

Compared to the average herd, the herds in the **High Forage** group used 0.6 tonne of concentrates less per year for each cow. Only about 30% of this reduction was accounted for by lower milk yields per cow. Most of the decrease in concentrate use was made possible through an increase in silage availability, coupled with an improvement in silage quality. As a result, the milk produced from forage was 1100 litres per cow greater than for the average DAIRYMAID herd.

The same is essentially true for the group of **Spring calving** herds. Concentrate use per cow was about 0.7 tonnes less than average and the milk obtained from forage was nearly 1200 litres per cow greater. Again the reduction in concentrate use and the increase in milk from forage was attributable in a large part to higher grass production and better utilisation of available grass through good grazing management. All this was reflected in higher profitability. Compared to the average, the potential margin over feed and forage for a herd producing 500,000 litres was projected to be 10.6% higher for the **Spring calving** group. The corresponding profit advantage for the **High Forage** group was 6.4%.

5.3 POTENTIAL FOR PROFITABLE MILK PRODUCTION FROM GRASS

The potential for profitable milk production, based on making maximum use of grass, is very high. This is shown in Table 5.1 for autumn and spring calving cows given silage of high quality (68D) and the minimum level of concentrates over the winter.

Recently, summer calving herds have become more popular. The aim is to produce milk during the high priced period from July to October, by calving cows in May, June and July. Details of the economic performance of such herds are not yet available. Economic analysis is difficult as summer calvers are often managed along with spring or autumn calving cows and margins are continually increasing as management practices for summer calvers improves. However, initial studies by the MMB demonstrated that margins over purchased feed for summer calving herds ranged from £650 to £900/cow, with the most profitable herds making maximum use of grass and feeding least concentrates during the winter.

Table 5.1 Potential for profitable milk production from grass under 'average' grass-growing conditions at 1989 prices.

	Autumn calvers	Spring calvers
Milk yield (litres/cow)	6000	6000
Concentrates (kg/cow)	1000	500
Nitrogen fertilizer (kg/ha)	350	350
Stocking rate (cows/ha)	2.4	2.2
UME (GJ/ha)	110	113
Margin over feed & forage		
pence/litre	14.12	14.95
£/cow	847.30	896.80
Gross margin (£/cow)	827.30	876.30

These targets show what can be achieved under average grass-growing conditions (Site Class 3) with minimal concentrate levels provided that:

- target levels of nitrogen are applied
- a well controlled system of grazing is operated
- silage is of high quality (68D)
- conservation is effectively integrated with grazing.

Making the best use of grass requires attention to all four, since the key to profitable dairy farming is not just growing grass but also effectively utilising it. This means getting the right balance between:

- nitrogen use
- stocking rate
- concentrate feeding
- milk yield

If the balance is wrong and the stocking rate is too low, grass will be wasted. If this is the case, then feed costs could be lowered by making greater use of available grass. On the other hand, if the stocking rate is too high, milk yields will fall and there is the danger that milk quotas may not be achieved.

For various combinations of nitrogen fertilizer and concentrate use, the appropriate stocking rates under 'average' grass-growing conditions (Site Class 3) for an autumn calving herd are shown in Table 5.2. The average milk yield of the cows in the herd is presumed to be 6000 litres. In each case it is assumed that **two** silage cuts are taken; the first at the end of May and the second towards the end of July to silage with a D-value of 61.

Table 5.2 **Target stocking rates at different inputs of nitrogen fertilizer and concentrates for an autumn calving herd under 'average' growing conditions (Site Class 3).**

Nitrogen (kg/ha)	Concentrates (tonnes/cow)						
	1.0	1.2	1.4	1.6	1.8	2.0	2.2
100	1.55	1.60	1.65	1.70	1.75	1.80	1.80
200	1.95	2.05	2.15	2.25[A]	2.30	2.35	2.40
300	2.25[B]	2.35	2.45	2.55[C]	2.65	2.75	2.85

How to use table

One example is for an autumn calving herd with an input of 1.6 tonnes of concentrates per cow at a stocking rate of 2.25 cows/ha. From Table 5.2 it can be seen that this stocking rate can be achieved with only 200 kg of nitrogen fertilizer per hectare (A). If less nitrogen is being used, then a shortage of grass for grazing or silage can be expected to occur, while if more is being applied, the aim should be to get a better performance by:

● reducing concentrate use

● increasing the stocking rate

● releasing some land for other crops or livestock enterprises.

For instance, increasing the fertilizer use to 300 kg/ha offers the possibility of increasing the overall profitability of the farm, for a given herd size and milk yield, by either:

● a reduction in concentrate use to 1.0 t/cow (B)

or

● increasing in the stocking rate to 2.55 cows/ha (C).

These various ways of obtaining greater profit are now discussed in more detail.

5.4 INCREASING PROFITS FROM GRASS - A CASE STUDY

Studies of grassland management on dairy farms have revealed three ways of improving output from grassland:

1. there is considerable scope for improving the **utilisation** of grass by the cows.

2. on many farms more grass can be grown by applying **additional nitrogen fertilizer**, leading to the production of more silage.

3. on most farms **silage quality** can be improved, permitting a reduction in the amount of concentrates fed to compensate for either low D-values or poor fermentation.

For a typical dairy farm, the implications of each of these possibilities are looked at below. Details about land use, nitrogen use, concentrate feeding, milk yields and stock numbers on this 'typical' farm in north-west England are shown in Table 5.3.

The dairy herd of 90 cows has no distinct season of calving and all replacements are reared on the farm. Winter requirements for silage are met by taking two conservation cuts, one in mid-June and the other in late July, producing 9.8 ME silage.

Table 5.3 Land use, purchased inputs, production and stock numbers on a representative farm.

LAND USE	65 hectares of grass
	15 hectares of potatoes and barley
STOCKING NUMBERS	90 dairy cows
	88 other cattle
STOCKING RATE	1.9 cows/hectare
NITROGEN USE	200 kg/hectare
CONCENTRATE USE	1.6 tonnes/cow
MILK YIELD	5250 litres/cow
ESTIMATED SILAGE PRODUCTION	1025 tonnes
ESTIMATED UME	65 Gigajoules/hectare
TOTAL FARM GRASS MARGIN	£ 69950
TOTAL FARM GROSS MARGIN	
LESS FORAGE HARVESTING COSTS	£ 62390

(a) Improving Grassland Utilisation

Feeding 1.6 tonnes of concentrates per cow and using 200 kg of nitrogen fertilizer per hectare, it should be possible to maintain a stocking rate of 2.25 cows per hectare according to Table 5.2. Compared to the actual stocking rate of 1.9 cows/ha, a possibility to increase the stocking density and releasing land for additional arable crops would therefore exist.

Alternatively, without increasing nitrogen use, the same stocking rate (1.9 cows/ha) could be maintained with a lower level of concentrates. On this farm, 400 out of 1600 kg of concentrates per cow are fed at grass. Much of this summer supplementation could be removed without affecting milk production. Even if grass availability is severely restricted and milk output is below quota, then silage rather than concentrates should be used to supplement the grass.

Comparison of the anticipated seasonal pattern of grass production with the amounts actually consumed by the cows suggests a third possibility, namely increasing overall silage production by adding a third cut in mid-September. Relative to the projected quantities of grass available in each month, the proportion estimated to be consumed by the cattle is shown in Figure 5.6.

Figure 5.6 Proportion of available grass apparently eaten by the herd in each month on the farm.

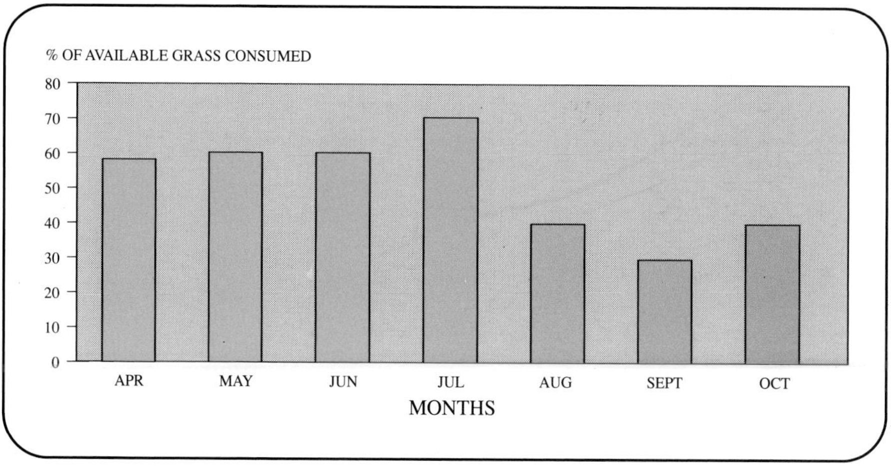

This figure reveals that in September under 50% of the available grass is apparently consumed. Thus, better utilization of the available grass in late summer/early autumn could be achieved by closing up some of the grass area for a conservation cut. In fact, about 11 hectares could be closed in August-September on this farm to produce 170 tonnes of additional silage. This would be sufficient to reduce concentrate use by about 400 kg/cow.

So, without increasing herd size, milk yields or nitrogen use, the farmer could improve grassland productivity on his farm by one of three actions:

1. keep the same stocking rate, but reduce concentrate levels from 1.6 to 1.2 tonnes/cow by feeding none to grazing cows.

2. keep the same stocking rate, but reduce concentrates from 1.6 to 0.8 tonnes/cow by a combination of making more silage through a third conservation cut and ceasing to feed concentrates at grass.

3. increase the stocking rate from 1.9 to 2.25 cows per hectare and release some of the existing grass area (11 ha) for additional barley and potatoes.

The effect of these actions on grassland productivity, as measured by the UME output per hectare and the overall farm gross margin, are shown in Figure 5.7. This shows that simply by making better use of available grass, without any increase in expenditure on fertilizer nitrogen, the farm margin can be increased by 9-17% or £5,500-£10,500. It should be noted that the benefits of releasing land for additional arable crops (3) may be overstated, as the farm gross margin figure ignores any fixed cost changes which might result.

Figure 5.7   Effect of making better use of available grass on the UME and farm gross margin.

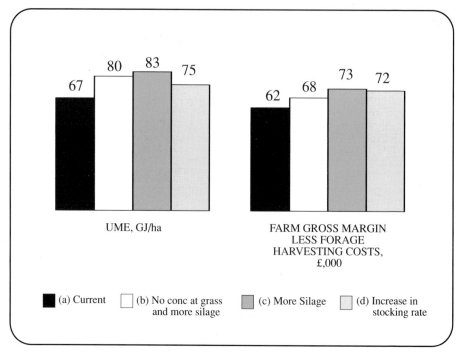

(b) Growing More Grass

With nitrogen use of only 200 kg/ha on this farm (see Table 5.3), opportunities clearly exist for an increase in overall fertilizer use. As before, the extra grass produced may be used to reduce concentrates or to release land for additional arable crops as a result of increasing the stocking density of the cows. For the same herd size and milk yield, the effects of increasing average nitrogen use from 200 to 300 kg/ha on the UME output and the farm gross margin are shown in Figure 5.8, for both courses of action. In each case, it is assumed that there is no overall improvement in the efficiency of grass utilization, as measured by the proportion of available grass which is consumed by the cows. In these circumstances, the extra grass produced by applying more nitrogen could be used to:

- reduce concentrate use from 1.6 to 1.0 t/cow
- increase the stocking density from 1.9 to 2.45 cows/ha, releasing additional land (15 ha) for additional barley and potatoes.

Figure 5.8 Effect of increasing nitrogen use from 200 to 300 kg/ha on UME output and the farm gross margin.

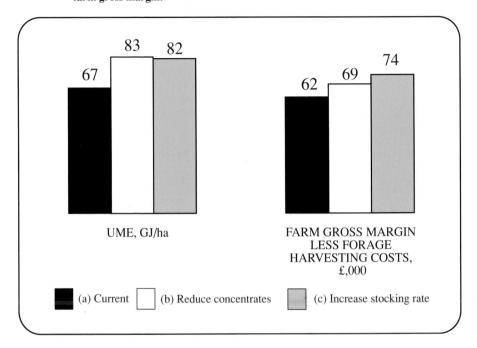

From Figure 5.8 it can be seen that increasing nitrogen use on the farm by 100 kg/ha might be expected to improve overall farm profits by 10-20% or £6000-£12000.

(c) Improving Silage Quality

Reductions in winter concentrate use can be achieved not just by making more silage, but also silage of higher D-value and better fermentation quality. This may involve taking more frequent conservation cuts and making the system less weather dependent through the use of additives. However, quantity should not be sacrificed for quality. One way of compensating for potentially lower grass yields as a result of aiming for higher quality silage is to use slightly more nitrogen and to take an autumn conservation cut.

Trials in Northern Ireland have shown that autumn calvers can achieve milk yields of 5250 litres with as little as 0.6 tonnes/cow of concentrates, as long as the cows are offered high quality (68D) silage. On the example farm (see Table 5.3) the silage is of fairly poor quality (61D) and in large part this is attributable to the date of cutting. By bringing forward the date of the first cut and increasing the number of cuts, better quality silage can be made. However, if the amount of concentrates fed in the winter is to be lowered, then nitrogen applications on the conservation areas will have to be increased to get the extra grass.

If fertilizer nitrogen is applied to the conservation areas at the rate of 100 kg/ha per cut, then the effect of bringing forward the first cut date to mid-May and taking two further cuts at 6-7 week intervals is to increase silage production by 1.3 tonnes per cow. Allowing for the improvement in both silage quality and quantity, concentrate use per cow could be reduced by 0.6 tonnes/cow. Additional fertilizer and silage harvesting costs of around £1000 would have to be set against this.

If a fourth conservation cut were to be taken in late September, then the overall silage production would be increased by a further 0.8 tonnes/cow at an extra cost for fertilizer and forage harvesting of £400. Against this, the extra silage would be sufficient to reduce concentrate use by a further 0.1 tonnes/cow.

The effect of improving silage quality, without assuming any increase in the efficiency of grass utilisation, on the UME output and farm gross margin for the example farm is shown in Figure 5.9.

Figure 5.9 Effect of improving silage quality on UME output and farm gross margin.

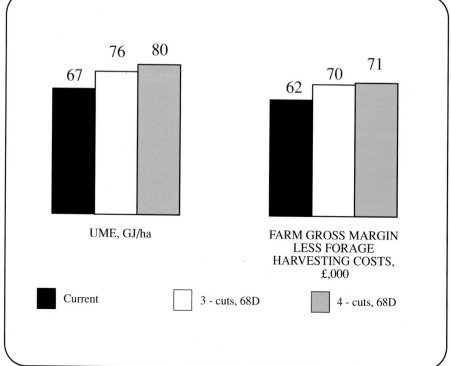

Improvements in silage quality could apparently increase profits on the farm by around 14% or £8000.

(d) Using White Clover

The use of mixed grass/white clover swards, with no or very few inputs of fertilizer nitrogen, as an alternative to grass/nitrogen systems has been discussed throughout this book. Using mixed swards can bring advantages in feeding value and milk production, although such positive responses have not always been observed in practice. A question therefore remains concerning the economic profitability of systems based on grass/clover. Studies in Scotland by the Scottish Agricultural College, suggest that a grass/clover system may not be more profitable than one based on grass/nitrogen, but mixed swards provide a viable alternative for dairy production systems. Details of the economic performance from the first two years of the study are presented in Table 5.4.

Both herds had a land area of 36 ha and 400000 litres of milk quota. The herds were autumn calving with Friesian/Holstein cows. No inorganic fertilizer nitrogen was used for the grass/clover pastures and 360 kg N/ha was applied to the grass/nitrogen area.

Mixed grass/white clover swards may provide a viable alternative to grass/nitrogen in areas where future legislation might restrict the use of fertilizer nitrogen. When clover is a high proportion of the botanical composition of swards (over 20% on a dry matter basis in mid season, see Chapter 1) it may provide up to 200 Kg N/ha over the growing season. Profitable milk production from mixed swards will be dependent on keeping a high proportion of clover in swards and management must aim to favour clover persistence. If reliance is placed solely on mixed swards, then a reduction in clover content would result in a rapid decline in herbage production and profitability.

Table 5.4 A comparison of financial performance for grass/clover and grass/ nitrogen systems.

	Grass/Clover		Grass/Nitrogen	
	1988/89	1989/90	1988/89	1989/90
No. cows	71	70	70	72
Milk sales (l/cow)	5658	5605	5764	5532
Total milk sales (l)	399566	392826	405855	399666
Concentrates (kg/cow)	1709	1554	1412	1185
Milk price (p/l)	18.13	18.98	18.03	18.99
MOFF (£/cow)	778	823	791	828
Gross margin (£/cow)	823	814	846	835
Gross margin (p/l)	14.55	14.49	14.68	15.12

(Bax, SAC)

5.4 PROFIT FROM GRASS - CONCLUSIONS

The opportunity exists for dairy farmers to make greater profits by means of:

1. Improved utilisation of available grass through better controlled grazing management.
2. Increased availability of both silage and grazed grass through increased applications of nitrogen fertilizer.
3. An improvement in silage quality through changes in the timing and frequency of conservation cuts.

The most profitable way of improving output from grassland will be influenced by individual farm circumstances. While it is not possible to provide specific advice on which course of action to follow, the decision rules involved in identifying the most profitable course of action are summarized in Figure 5.10.

Figure 5.10 A guide to the most profitable way of improving output from grassland.

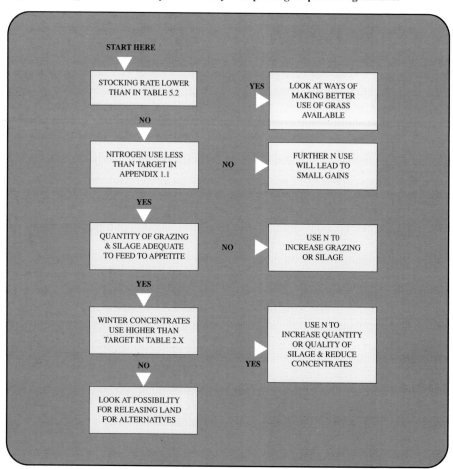

In summary, the three basic rules for profitable grassland management are:

● apply target levels of nitrogen
● achieve the correct balance between concentrates, nitrogen fertilizer and stocking rate
● closely integrate conservation with grazing.

APPENDIX 1: GRASS PRODUCTION

1.1: GRASS YIELD

Yield (tonnes of dry matter per hectare) of late perennial ryegrass from different cutting strategies under different grass growing conditions (Site Classes).

	"Target" N				
Site Class	1	2	3	4	5
3 Cuts at 68D					
Cut on 18 May	4.7	4.5	4.3	4.5	4.2
22 June	4.3	3.7	3.4	2.8	2.8
27 July	2.9	2.8	2.6	2.4	2.3
Autumn Grazing	3.4	3.3	2.9	2.8	2.3
Total	**15.3**	**14.3**	**13.2**	**12.5**	**11.6**
4 Cuts at 68D					
Cut on 18 May	4.7	4.5	4.3	4.5	4.2
22 June	4.3	3.7	3.4	2.8	2.8
27 July	3.9	2.8	2.6	2.4	2.3
31 August	2.2	2.9	2.4	2.1	1.7
Autumn Grazing	0.3	0.3	0.3	0.3	0.3
Total	**15.4**	**14.2**	**13.0**	**12.1**	**11.3**
1 Cut at 68D with **2 regrowths cut at 65D**					
Cut on 18 May	4.7	4.5	4.3	4.5	4.2
2 July	6.3	5.4	4.8	4.2	3.9
16 August	2.7	3.0	3.1	3.0	2.7
Autumn Grazing	1.6	1.4	1.2	1.0	0.8
Total	**15.3**	**14.3**	**13.4**	**12.7**	**11.6**

Site Class	1	2	3	4	5
2 Cuts at 65D					
Cut on 29 May	7.0	6.8	6.4	6.3	6.0
13 July	3.6	2.8	2.6	2.5	2.5
Autumn Grazing	4.0	3.6	3.2	2.8	2.4
Total	**14.6**	**13.2**	**12.2**	**11.6**	**10.9**
1 Cut at 65D plus					
1 Cut at 63D					
Cut on 29 May	7.0	6.8	6.4	6.3	6.0
23 July	4.6	3.9	3.6	3.4	3.3
Autumn Grazing	3.7	3.5	3.3	2.8	2.5
Total	**15.3**	**14.2**	**13.3**	**12.5**	**11.8**
2 Cuts at 61D					
Cut on 10 June	9.3	9.1	8.5	8.1	7.7
12 August	4.6	4.2	4.0	3.7	3.5
Autumn Grazing	2.1	2.0	1.8	1.6	1.4
Total	**16.0**	**15.3**	**14.3**	**13.4**	**12.6**
1 Cut at 61D					
Cut on 10 June	9.3	9.1	8.5	8.1	7.7
Autumn Grazing	4.7	4.2	3.6	3.1	2.6
Total	**14.0**	**13.3**	**12.1**	**11.2**	**10.3**

1.2 APPLICATION RATES OF NITROGEN FOR GRASSLAND

Grazed Swards

	Nitrogen applications for intensive grazing (kg/ha) (Medium soil N status)					
			Every 4 weeks following grazing			
Site class	Pre-grazing Split dressing	1	2	3	4	Total
1	55/75	90	70	70	70	430
2	55/65	80	60	60	60	380
3	55/55	70	50	50	50	320
4	55/55	60	40	40	40	300
5	55/45	50	35	35	35	255

Responses are greatest in early season and daily rates up to 4 kg nitrogen per hectare per day can sometimes be justified. Thereafter, worthwhile responses are only likely for rates of 1.5 - 2.5 kg N/ha or less. The recommendations are to apply most nitrogen in the spring as responses are high and losses lower at this time of the year. The first application of the split dressing should be made about 7 weeks before normal turnout date, and the second application 2 weeks before turnout. However, if the first application is delayed because of adverse soil and weather conditions until 4 weeks or less before normal turnout, a single application should be made and the recommended rate reduced at all site classes by 30 kg N/ha.

If prolonged periods without rainfall occur resulting in no significant growth for grazing at the expected time the next application should be reduced or omitted. Applications after mid-August may have major effects on nitrate levels in the soil with subsequent loss in drainage water over winter. In the interests of minimising losses and adverse environmental effects the last application, which was recommended in the first edition of this book, has been omitted. Whilst an economic response may be obtained from an application of 40 Kg N/ha in late August, it is not recommended.

Conserved Swards

The appropriate rates of nitrogen to apply for conservation cuts taken at high D value in a 3 cut system or moderate D value in a 2 cut system are shown in the tables below. It is assumed that the fields will have been cut and grazed in recent years and have a medium soil N status.

Nitrogen applications for a 2 cut conservation system (kg/ha)

Site class	1st cut Late May/ early June	2nd cut Late July	Grazing applied late July	Total
1	50/100	150	70	370
2	50/100	140	60	350
3	50/90	130	60	340
4	50/80	120	50	300
5	50/80	110	40	280

An additional 40 Kg N/ha may be applied for a second grazing application, but this should not be applied after mid August.

Nitrogen applications for a 3 cut conservation system (kg/ha)

Site class	1st cut mid-May	2nd cut late June	3rd cut Early August	1st grazing Applied early August	Total
1	50/90	140	90	50	420
2	50/80	130	90	50	400
3	50/70	120	90	50	380
4	50/70	110	90	50	370
5	50/60	100	80	40	330

For first cut silage some fertilizer should be applied mid-February to early March, approximately 12 weeks before cutting and the remainder 4 weeks later. If weather conditions prevent an early application and fertilizer is applied some weeks before cutting there will be no advantage to applying a single dressing. Should the delay in application result in less than 8 weeks to the anticipated cutting date the quantity applied should be reduced by 20 kg/ha for each further delay of a week. When slurry has been applied to conservation fields in the spring the quantities shown should be reduced by 30 - 40 kg N/ha. (see page 25).

Pattern of Application of Nitrogen for Cut Grass

The recommended rate of nitrogen for a first cut of silage is between 100 and 150 kg N/ha, depending on the site class and soil nitrogen status. There is no advantage to applying more if the crop is being left slightly longer to bulk up for lower quality silage. The first cut provides the majority of the grass for the winter on all farms.

For second cuts the target rate of nitrogen is similar to that for first cuts on site class 1 but slightly lower on other site classes reflecting the lower availability of water. If a heavy and late first cut has been taken second cuts in some areas can be disappointing. The 'second cut' may receive up to 125 kg N/ha if the field has been previously grazed.

Grass which is to be returned to the grazing area after cutting should receive slightly more nitrogen than the remainder of the grazed grass, 40 to 80 kg N/ha, depending on site class, but not more than 40 Kg N/ha in August and no fertilizer N should be applied later than mid August.

Fertilizer should be applied **immediately** after the crop is removed from the field.

Effect of Soil N Status on Target N

The effect of having a high soil N status is to reduce the need for fertilizer N by 50 kg/ha. Conversely, a low soil N status increases the need for fertilizer nitrogen by 70 kg/ha. Differences in responses between sites are fairly uniform across the growing season and it is recommended that proportionate changes are made in nitrogen usage at each harvest.

APPENDIX 2

2.1 Silage and Concentrate Requirements

SILAGE REQUIREMENTS AND MINIMUM CONCENTRATE INPUTS TO ACHIEVE 6000 l/cow*

	Autumn Calvers D-value (No. of Cuts)			Spring Calvers D-value (No. of Cuts)		
	61 (1/2)	64/65/ (2)	67/68 (3/4)	61 (1/2)	64/65/ (2)	67/68 (3/4)
Winter concentrates/cow (t fresh weight)	1.38	1.15	0.92	0.79	0.59	0.45
Silage requirement/cow						
– dry matter (t)	1.70	1.87	2.02	1.80	1.95	1.98
– fresh at 25% dry matter (t)	6.80	7.48	8.08	7.20	7.72	7.92
Grass requirement/cow**						
– dry matter (t)	2.04	2.24	2.42	2.16	2.32	2.38
– fresh at 25% dry matter (t)	8.16	8.96	9.68	8.64	9.28	9.52

* Calculated for 180 day winter   ** Silage requirement plus 20% for losses in conservation

(H. StC. Neal, IGER)

2.2 Areas to be closed up for conservation (ha/Cow) at target fertilizer N for different site classes and cutting regimes based on minimum concentrate for cows yielding 6000 litres

Silage Strategy	Time	Site Class	Autumn Calvers			Spring Calvers		
			1	3	5	1	3	5
68D (4 Cuts)	Up to mid May		0.26	0.32	0.39	0.27	0.34	0.40
(Mid May/mid	Mid May to mid June		0.24	0.22	0.23	0.23	0.22	0.21
June/mid August)	Mid June to mid July		0.24	0.22	0.23	0.23	0.22	0.21
	Mid July to mid August		0.26	0.25	0.27	0.19	0.15	0.12
67D (3 Cuts	Up to mid May		0.25	0.32	0.38	0.27	0.34	0.40
Mid May/end June	Mid May to end June		0.22	0.22	0.21	0.25	0.22	0.21
/mid August	End June to mid August		0.23	0.22	0.21	0.18	0.15	0.12
64D (2 Cuts)	Up to end May		0.23	0.27	0.31	0.24	0.28	0.32
(End May/end July)	End May to end July		0.20	0.20	0.21	0.20	0.21	0.21
61D (2 Cuts)	Up to mid June		0.17	0.19	0.32	0.19	0.22	0.25
Mid June/end August)	Mid June to end August		0.17	0.19	0.23	0.14	0.15	0.16
61D (1 Cut) (Mid June)	Up to mid June		0.22	0.25	0.29	0.25	0.26	0.30

APPENDIX 5

Appendix 5 Measures of Financial Efficiency

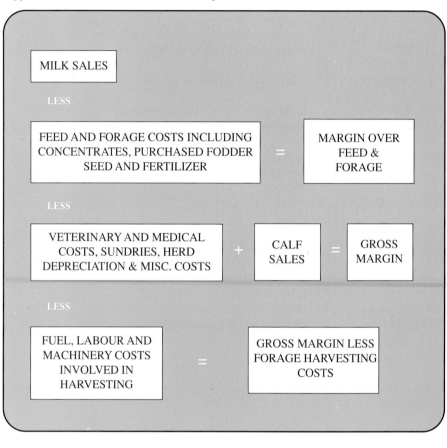

LIST OF CONTRIBUTORS

R.D. BAKER	Station Secretary	**IGER**
C.J. DOYLE	Economics and Marketing Department	**SAC**
G.E.J. FISHER	Grassland and Ruminant Science Department	**SAC**
S. GOLDIE	The Botanic Centre, Middlesbrough, *formerly ICI*	
M.E. HUTCHINSON	Kings Hey Trust for Farming and Conservation, *formerly ICI*	
H. LIDGATE	Agricultural Consultant, *formerly ICI*	
C.S. MAYNE	Agricultural Research Institute of Northern Ireland	**ARINI**
A. REEVE	Technical Development Manager	**ICI**
C. THOMAS	Grassland and Ruminant Science Department	**SAC**